5-8-68

SEALS OF THE WORLD

Northern Fur Seals

World Wildlife Series 2

SEALS

OF THE WORLD

Gavin Maxwell

Illustrated with Photographs

HOUGHTON MIFFLIN COMPANY BOSTON

1967

Acknowledgments

My chief debt is to my two scientific collaborators, John Stidworthy and David Williams, who undertook a great deal of library research in collecting material on the thirty-two species of Pinnipeds.

I am grateful to Macmillan & Company for permission to quote the two poems by Rudyard Kipling in Chapter II. The names of the photographers are given in the List of Illustrations. Between them they have provided studies of twenty-eight of the thirty-two species.

Contents

Illustrations

The World Wildlife Fund

The World Wildlife Fund is an international charitable foundation for raising money to save the world's wildlife and wild places. It is devoted to the concept that conservation is for the benefit of man, who has ethical, aesthetic and economic responsibilities to preserve at least part of the natural environment in which he has evolved. At one end of its scale of activities it is trying to save certain animal and plant species from imminent extinction — a kind of modern Noah's Ark; at the other it extends over the whole intricate relationship between water, soil, plants, animals and man himself. It is concerned with the right use of land — in short with the *Ecology of Man*.

Man must learn to apply the science of ecology to himself. He must also recognize that he has responsibilities in this context — responsibilities of trusteeship for the natural world over which he now exercises so much control. Take, for example, oil pollution and fresh-water pollution, and toxic chemical sprays; and take the extermination of animal and plant species — an utterly irrevocable process. . . .

At this moment more than a thousand kinds of vertebrate animals are threatened with imminent extinction at the hands of man. Species which have taken hundreds of thousands of years to evolve their unique adaptations to their environment are being wiped out in a few decades because they do not seem to have a 'use', or because not enough people care one way or the other.

The World Wildlife Fund was set up under Swiss Federal Law on 28th September, 1961, with an announcement that the wildlife situation in the world at large amounted to 'a state of emergency for animals' and with the publication of a World Wildlife Charter for submission to the United Nations.

The British National Appeal of the World Wildlife Fund (which is established as a Charity for tax purposes) has Prince Philip as its President.

To fulfil its aims and ambitions, the World Wildlife Fund urgently requires money. Any contributions or enquiries should be addressed to:

The Director General,
The World Wildlife Fund (British National Appeal),
7/8 Plumtree Court,
London EC4.

The address of the headquarters in Switzerland is:

The Secretary-General,
World Wildlife Fund (International),
Morges,
Vaud.

1 . What Makes a Seal

There are thirty-two, or perhaps now only thirty-one, living species of seal, ranging in size from the little Ringed Seal, less than 5 feet long, up to the giant Elephant Seals which may be 20 feet long and 4 tons in weight. All are highly adapted for life in the water, but they have not left the land behind so completely as the other aquatic orders of mammals, the whales and the sea-cows. The seals have streamlined bodies to assist their movement through the water but they still retain all four limbs of their terrestrial ancestors, whereas whales have one pair only. Seals can leave the water and move on land, albeit clumsily, and practically all of them must come on land to give birth to their young. However, most of their life is spent in the water; this is where they are most at home, and this is where they obtain their food. The diet of seals is almost entirely carnivorous, as probably was that of their ancestors.

At one time the seals were thought to be sufficiently closely related to land-living, meat-eating mammals to be placed with them in a single classificatory group, the order Carnivora. Nowadays, instead of leaving the seals as a sub-group of the Carnivora, many zoologists place them in a separate order of their own, the Pinnipedia. This is really only two ways of looking at the same set of facts, but the modern view does recognise that although seals have much in common with such animals as bears and wolves they are sharply divided from them by the considerable modifications they have undergone to suit their watery habitat — as is suggested by their name Pinnipedia, 'the fin-footed ones.' A member of the Pinnipedia can be recognised at a glance by its flippers and shape.

When the Pinnipedia are looked at carefully, however, it becomes apparent that not just one type but three main types of animal are included in the order. There are firstly the true seals, secondly the sealions and fur seals, and lastly, by itself, the walrus. It is quite easy to distinguish a sealion from a seal. The true seals, the family Phocidae, have no earflaps, the external part of the ear having been sacrificed to the necessary streamlining of the body. When a seal swims, the propulsive force comes from a strong sculling action of the hind-flippers. These always remain pointing back from the hind end of the body, even when the animal is on land, so that they are useless for locomotion on terra firma. True seals also have fur-covered flippers with nails about the same size on each toe, testes within the body wall, and either two or four teats on the mammary glands.

In contrast, the fur seals and sealions, the family Otariidae, although their ears externally are very much reduced for streamlining, still retain a small and obvious earflap protruding from the side of the head, and for this reason they are sometimes called otaries, or eared seals. These animals also differ in their means of locomotion. Most of the power for swimming comes from the fore-limbs which are powerful paddles, while the hindlimbs are rarely active. On the other hand the hindlimbs can be brought underneath the body of a sealion when it is on land, and it can stand on four legs or even manage a kind of gallop. The flippers of otaries are bare of fur, usually black-skinned, and with only rudimentary nails, at least on the foreflipper. There are always four mammary teats and the testes are outside the body wall in a scrotal sac.

The Walrus is put in a family by itself, the Odobenidae, because it seems to fall between the two other families in its characteristics, although it is probably closer to the sealions than to the seals. It has no earflaps, its testes are internal, but it has bare flippers, can get its hindflippers under its body when walking, and swims mainly, but not exclusively, by employing forelimbs rather than hindlimbs.

It is not known exactly how or where the Pinnipedia originated but they undoubtedly arose from land carnivores, and from those of the Canoid (dog-bear-weasel) side of the group rather than from the Feloid (cat-mongoose-hyaena) type. The pinnipeds have left no missing-link fossils to tell of their origins. The earliest fossils we have come from about twenty million years ago, during the Miocene period, and the bony remains show animals that were already definite pinnipeds, not so very different from some of the animals alive today. It is not even certain that the Phocidae and Otariidae had a common ancestor and indeed many of their characteristics suggest that they may have developed separately, but in parallel ways, from different ancestors. This would seem to destroy the apparent midway position of the walrus. Some zoologists who support an origin of the pinnipeds from two distinct sources consider that the Otariids probably had an ancestor in common with the otters, animals which they have long outstripped in their mastery of the water. Phocids have probably been around longer than Otariids as their bodies are in some ways more completely modified from the typical land carnivore pattern.

At present pinnipeds are found in all the oceans of the world but they are most abundant, in both numbers of species and numbers of individuals, in the seas around the Arctic and Antarctic. Tropical waters, in most cases, seem an effective barrier to their spread, although at some stage in their evolution this barrier must have been crossed. There are exceptions, notably the Monk Seals, but most populations of seals live in polar seas or in parts of other seas subject to the influence of cold currents. The correlation between the presence of cold currents and the presence of pinnipeds along the coasts of the continents is very striking. Off south-west Africa, for example, the Benguela current exerts its cooling effect and the South African Fur Seal is present. Off the west coast of South America up as far as the Galapagos Islands runs the cold Humboldt current, and pinnipeds are present. The Labrador current, the California current, the Falkland current and Oyashio current all provide cold waters inhabited by seals. As a general rule the Phocids are found in the coldest waters of all; fur seals in cold but not polar waters, in the southern hemisphere and north Pacific; and sealions in the warmer waters of the Pacific where they probably originated. The differing distribution seems to reflect the extent to which these pinnipeds are insulated against the cold, but whether the insulation is a consequence of the distribution is problematical. Parts of the Arctic and Antarctic oceans contain abundant plankton for the seals or their prey, and this may partly account for their occurrence in these places.

It is essential for any warm-blooded animal that spends long periods in the water to have a covering which will insulate the body from the surrounding cold. Any animal that failed to do this would soon suffer a massive heat loss for which it could not compensate. The pinnipeds have solved the problem in two basic ways.

The true seals have the normal mammalian covering of hair which on land prevents the loss of heat by trapping an insulating layer of air next to the skin. In the water this hair is of little account as it soon becomes soaked and the water comes in contact with the skin. Excessive heat loss in the water is prevented by a thick layer of fat (blubber) under the skin. Fat is a reasonably good insulator and a thickness of the order of three inches, which is what most seals have, is very effective indeed. The metabolism of seals, too, is much faster than in most land mammals and this readily enables them to make up for losses in heat. One would imagine that a flat, thin piece of body such as a flipper would give off heat particularly fast, but in fact loss from the flippers is minimised by the arrangement of the blood vessels in them. These vessels are arranged in a network devised in such a way that the warm blood flowing *into* the flipper passes very close to the vessels taking blood *out of* the flipper; the inflowing blood loses most of its heat to the outflowing blood, so that the flippers and the blood in them are generally at a lower temperature than the rest of the seal's body when in the water, and heat is not wasted in an effort to keep them warm.

A seal does not attempt to keep the surface of its skin warm in the water. The skin is well supplied with small blood vessels but these can be shut off from the main circulation if necessary and in cold water most of these vessels are closed — only enough blood is allowed through to stop the skin from freezing and to give it nourishment. The inside of a seal's body is then as well insulated as the fluid inside a vacuum flask, with the added advantage that it can generate heat of its own. The inside of a seal from about one-and-a-half inches below the surface may be at 37°C. but the outer part of its skin in freezing water may be at only 2°C. — a massive temperature gradient resulting in little heat lost to the water. Thus even in very cold temperatures an Arctic seal has no need to increase its metabolism.

On the occasions that seals need to get rid of excess heat — during periods of vigorous exercise or basking in warm sun — they can do this quite simply by dilating the blood vessels in the skin and losing heat from the body surface.

Normally pieces of dead skin are constantly flaking off mammals, but for a seal an easily waterlogged outer layer would be an inconvenience. Seals avoid this by sloughing off skin and hair for only a short period of the year, often hauling out on land while the moult lasts. In some Phocids, such as Elephant Seals, the skin comes off in large patches with hair attached.

Fur seals have a different method of insulating the body. Their fur is very thick and is grown as two distinct layers. The upper layer consists of long, coarse guard hairs. The shorter, lower layer is very much finer and serves as the main insulation in the coat; even under water it traps bubbles of air which help to cut down the outflow of heat. When a fur seal moults, its hairs drop out singly but not all the underfur hairs come out of the skin, so as a fur seal gets older its coat tends to become thicker. Fur seals also have a thick layer of blubber under the skin. They do not have the elaborate skin modifications of Phocids for regulating blood flow.

A fur seal is thus well insulated but, on land at least, there is always danger of it overheating if it is very active. The only scope for heat loss in a fur seal lies in its bare flippers, and in panting. Like true seals their flippers have a network of small blood vessels. These cut down heat loss most of the time, but blood can probably be sent through other channels close to the surface if heat needs to be lost. The flippers are usually black, a good colour for radiating heat, and they have many sweat glands. When fur seals are hot after exertion on land they wave their flippers in the air like fans.

Sealions probably have a less effective insulation than seals or fur seals because their coat is simply hair (like that of the Phocids) without underfur, and although they have blubber they do not seem to have the highly adapted skins of true seals. Their poorer insulation may explain why they generally occur in warmer climates than other pinnipeds.

Walruses have almost bare skins and must rely on their blubber for warmth.

In order to breed, seals have to overcome a number of problems inherent in their environment. Firstly, contact between the sexes has to be assured in a population which may be dispersed over thousands of square miles of ocean. Most species have solved this problem by the establishment of special breeding grounds on land or ice, a limited number in each case, so that when the seals return to them they are certain of contact with their own kind. Most seals have a well-developed homing instinct and return year after year to the same ground, very often the place of their birth. Most seals, too, have a well-defined and short breeding season so that all the seals of a colony come together at the same time, and this period allows the females both to give birth and — almost immediately afterwards — to mate again. In harsh environments the breeding season must be timed to give the youngsters the best chance of surviving. This usually means that they are born in the latter part of winter or the beginning of spring (November–December in the southern hemisphere, March–April in the

B

northern) and take to the water in the spring and summer, a season when plankton — and therefore the seal's prey — is more abundant. The puppyhood of seals is short, a factor which drastically reduces the most vulnerable period of life. Most pinnipeds are born in an advanced state — many have resorbed and lost their milk teeth before birth, some have lost their puppy coat in the uterus, some can swim a few hours after birth — but most are born pathetically thin, with scarcely any blubber. This defect is partially compensated for by a thick woolly coat, but many seal pups still shiver vigorously. Seals grow at an incredible rate, however, especially those in very cold regions. The blubber of the mother is converted to milk and transferred to the pup, which uses it for rapid growth and reconverts it to blubber for food storage and insultation. It is noticeable that the pinnipeds from the coldest environments usually have the shortest lactation period (two to three weeks in many polar seals, compared to six months for a sealion) and also the most concentrated milk, so the infancy of these seals is very short — a good protective adaptation. Seal milk is different from the milk of land mammals but similar to that of whales; it contains no sugars but has a very high concentration of fat (making it rather viscous) and also a large proportion of protein, all factors promoting rapid growth in the pup.

To synchronise pupping with the right period of the year seals have developed the physiological device of delayed implantation. The fertilised ovum begins to develop immediately after copulation, but when it reaches the blastocyst stage of development it becomes dormant. The embryo of most mammals becomes implanted in the lining of the uterus when it reaches this stage, but in the case of the seals the blastocyst remains free in the uterus for several weeks or months before it implants and development continues. In this way birth can be synchronised with the annual breeding season. The gestation period of seals is a little under a year but includes two phases — first the period of delayed implantation, and then the 'true' gestation period, which differs from species to species. Delayed implantation has been found in all the seal species which have been thoroughly investigated. (Delayed implantation also occurs among other mammals, such as bats and some of the weasel family, but in their case the reason for timing the season of birth in this way remains obscure.) Cow seals bear a single pup at a time, although very occasionally twin foetuses are discovered when a cow is dissected. There are a few records of the live birth of twins, for example by Southern Elephant Seals and Northern Fur Seals.

All the Otariids have developed territorial and polygamous habits in the breeding season, but only the Elephant Seals and Grey Seal among the Phocids. The most vigorous bulls defend the best territories or largest harems and thus the strongest fathers sire the majority of the pups. The males of the polygamous species are usually considerably larger than the females, and the biggest discrepancy in size is among those which form the largest harems. The female of other pinnipeds is about the same size as, or fractionally larger than, the male.

A penis bone or baculum is present in the pinnipeds. It is small in young males but grows as the animal becomes older, the fastest growth taking place around the time of attaining sexual maturity.

Because seals often return to their birthplace to breed it is not surprising that many colonies breeding in isolation have developed their own individual characteristics — different times of breeding, or different breeding sites. It is true for many species that there is considerable variation between individuals in colour and even such things as skull shape and the number of teeth (which in most animals are reasonably constant), but for the most part the characteristics of seal species are surprisingly constant between colonies. Until the coming of man most seals bred in places safe from danger or disturbance and this may have led to a less stringent selection by the environment of one 'design' in preference to others. Like many species of land mammals several species of seal form 'clines' — there is a gradual change in some of the characteristics of the species between one end of its range and the other. Sometimes this leads authorities to name several subspecies, but often there is no distinct line to be drawn between one subspecies and the next. Colour differences between pinnipeds are always a little unreliable; a wet coat will look quite unlike a dry coat even if both are exactly the same colour.

All seals are carnivores. Probably none deliberately ingest plantstuffs. Not all seals eat fish — some feed on crustaceans and for many the favourite food is squid. The fish eaters mainly have sharp pointed teeth but those that eat invertebrates often have rather rudimentary teeth.

The number and grouping of the teeth (dentition) is very varied within the pinnipeds. Molars and premolars are not usually distinguished.

Otariidæ (Sealions and fur seals)

incisors 3 each side top jaw	canines 1 each side top jaw	post-canines 5 or 6 top jaw
3 each side lower jaw	1 each side lower jaw	5 each side lower jaw

making a total of 34 or 36, but there are variations between individuals.

Odobenidæ (Walrus)

incisors $\dfrac{1}{0}$ canines $\dfrac{1}{1}$ post-canines $\left.\dfrac{3}{3}\right\}$ making a total of 18, with variations

Phocidæ (Seals)

Northern Seals   incisors $\dfrac{3}{2}$ canines $\dfrac{1}{1}$ post-canines $\left.\dfrac{5}{5}\right\{$ usual total 34 but some may be lost

Monk Seals   incisors $\dfrac{2}{2}$ canines $\dfrac{1}{1}$ post-canines $\left.\dfrac{5}{5}\right\{$ normal total 32

Bladdernosed Seals incisors $\dfrac{2}{1}$ canines $\dfrac{1}{1}$ post-canines $\left.\dfrac{5}{5}\right\{$ normal total 30

Seals tend to have long intestines, a fact which has not been adequately explained. Carnivorous animals on the whole tend to have proportionately much shorter intestines than their vegetarian counterparts as their food is much easier to digest. The intestine of a dog, for example, is about five times its body length whereas that of an ox is some twenty times the length of its body. For most seals the figure is well over ten times and sometimes considerably more. The function of this long gut is a mystery but the digestion of seals is certainly fast and it is rare to find one returning from a hunting trip and hauling out with a full stomach – the food has already been digested. The longest intestines of all seem to belong to those seals which eat predominantly squid. Perhaps this requires strong digestion.

A large proportion of seals have been found with stones in the stomach. There has been a lot of speculation about this, but perhaps the stones are necessary to regulate the animals' buoyancy and swimming posture. Crocodiles also swallow stones — apparently to lower their buoyancy.

Wild seals probably drink very little intentionally. Captive pinnipeds have been known to drink fresh water, but as they have saltier blood than land mammals they are probably able to cope with the sea water they must inevitably swallow. Those seals which eat fish probably get most of their water from their prey. This is less saline than sea water, though seals which eat salty invertebrates must find it more difficult to avoid dehydration.

Not very much work has been done on seals to determine how well their various sense organs function. A few seals are said to have a good sense of smell but as all seals keep their nostrils closed under water, and for much of the time on land, this sense cannot be of much importance, except to help cows identify their pups.

The eyes of seals are mostly large, although some species undoubtedly have better vision than others. Most have brown, liquid-looking eyes with a small but expansible pupil and an almost transparent iris in which the blood vessels can be seen. Some of the species which dive deeply or live under ice have huge eyeballs in proportion to their skull and in dark places they probably open the pupils wide to let in as much light as possible. Seals' eyes work better under water than in air and can apparently accommodate much better than the human eye to the change of focus entailed in moving from water to air and back again. To function efficiently in water the lens of a seal has to be very thick and rather spherical — the cornea is of no help in focussing light on the retina as the inside of the eye and the water surrounding it are of a similar refractive index. A peculiarity of the seal's eye is the lack of the tear duct, running from eye to nose, which is found in land mammals; as a result the seal, when it is on land and its fur is dry, always looks as though it is crying, tears constantly spilling out of the eye and running down the face.

There is little doubt that many seals catch at least part of their food by sight, but sight is not always indispensable to a seal. There are various records of totally blind seals found in a perfectly healthy and well-fed condition and these must have found their food in other ways. Probably the whiskers (and eyebrows too in a Phocid) are important sense organs. The whiskers have nerves at their bases, and if they are moved by a disturbance in the water the seal can sense the disturbance. This sense could be used for hunting and is probably important for seals in turbid waters, as in the case of the Common Seals that live in the waters of the Wash, which are sometimes muddy.

Perhaps hearing is the most important sense. Although lacking large earflaps, the ears of seals inside the head are large and well-developed. In water sound travels far better than in air and it would be surprising if seals did not make use of this. When submerged, the tube leading from the seal's eardrum to the outside is closed, partly by muscular action and partly by water pressure, but the seal can still hear. Sounds may be conducted along the wall of this meatus even with the ear closed (as happens in some whales) but in any case it is not essential for an animal under water to have exterior receiving apparatus in order to register sounds.

Recordings have been made of underwater sounds emitted by pinnipeds; these showed that some seals (including the Californian Sealion, the Common Seal and the Grey Seal), in addition to the usual barks and grunts which are audible to the human ear, also produce high frequency sound pulses. These are similar to the sounds produced for echolocation by dolphins in water and by bats in air, and it may well be that they are used by seals for the same reason, although they only seem strong enough for use at short range. This may provide another explanation for the ability of blind seals to feed well.

All the pinnipeds are streamlined for easy movement through the water. Their blubber helps to round off their contours nicely, and also increases buoyancy — an asset to some seals.

Phocid seals swim by using their hindflippers for power. These are held apart and sculled from side to side, the leading flipper 'feathered" and the following one, widely spread, pushing hard against the water as it moves towards the midline. Because of the flipper's flexibility most of the push is directed backwards and the seal moves forward. Much of the muscle in a Phocid is in the lumbar region where the vertebrae allow considerable movement in all directions.

As in most aquatic vertebrates the bony processes by which one vertebra articulates with another are very much reduced. In pinnipeds there are 40 to 42 vertebrae, the number of tail vertebrae being variable. [Vertebrae as follows: Cervical 7; Thoracic 15 (14 in Walrus); Lumbar 5 (6 in Walrus); Sacral 3; Caudal 10–12].

The thigh bone (femur) of seals is short, the main development being of the outer parts of the hindlimb. The foreflipper is short and only the bones equivalent to the human hand project from the surface of the body. When a Phocid seal is swimming the foreflippers are usually flattened to the body in depressions corresponding to armpits, so they do not interfere with streamlining. They are used only for steering and manoeuvring. On land the northern Phocids can flex the ends of the foreflipper digits and grip and pull themselves along with them. There is no collarbone, and this allows the flipper sufficient mobility to scratch from nosetip to belly.

The Otariids swim in a rather different way. The whole 'forearm' and 'hand' project from the body and form the large flipper used for propulsion. The hindlimbs are relatively unimportant in the water. Much of the muscle is thus concentrated in the foreflipper region, resulting in bulky forequarters.

The Walrus uses a combination of Phocid and Otariid methods when swimming, but foreflippers are probably the more important.

Both Phocids and Otariids are capable of speeds as high as 15–18 m.p.h. in short bursts.

As well as being agile swimmers the pinnipeds are excellent divers. It is, of course, very difficult to find how deep a wild seal will dive but a Grey Seal has been caught on a hook that was nearly 500 feet below the surface, a Harp Seal in a net at 600 feet and another on a hook at 825 feet. Two Bladder-nosed Seals taken alive for Bremerhaven Zoo are said to have been caught at 1200 feet and 1260 feet. Recent observations in Antarctica have shown that Weddell Seals may go down as far as 1500 feet and commonly choose a depth of 750 to 1000 feet when swimming underwater. Seals may dive to even greater depths — many species are capable of remaining submerged for twenty minutes, and some can stay under for half an hour or longer. A dive of over forty-three minutes has been timed for the Weddell Seal.

How do seals manage such long dives when a human diver is considered excellent if he can manage much over two minutes? Seals have plenty of blood and the blood contains plenty of oxygen. A seal has about one-and-a-half times the blood of a land mammal of similar size. In addition much oxygen is stored in the pigment myoglobin of the seal's muscles — this is similar to haemoglobin and gives seal meat its dark red colour. Even with these stores of oxygen seals would not be able to stay down very long if they used up oxygen as fast as they do at the surface, but oxygen consumption is cut down by shutting off all the blood vessels going to the muscles and just maintaining a flow to a few essential organs, especially the brain. When the seal dives and shuts its nose a reflex slows down the heartbeat from 150 beats a minute (the normal rate on the surface) to only ten beats a minute. The deeper the dive the slower the heartbeat. Round the main vein returning blood to the heart (the posterior vena cava), just before it reaches the diaphragm, there is a ring of muscle, and when a seal dives this probably tightens up and restricts the flow of blood back to the heart. So a seal's metabolism slows down considerably when it dives and the blood circulates slowly to eke out the available oxygen. Since a seal in the water is in a state of neutral buoyancy it requires little energy to manoeuvre with.

Most mammals have a region in the brain which causes the animal to draw breath by reflex action as soon as there is a certain concentration of carbon dioxide in the blood. This respiratory centre in the seal is relatively insensitive, and the animal tolerates much more carbon dioxide in its blood than do other mammals before it is forced to take a breath.

Much of the energy produced by muscles during a dive is derived from processes which do not require oxygen. The final stage in the 'burning' of the food takes place after the seal has surfaced again, opened its nostrils, taken in fresh oxygen, and restored the blood supply and hence the oxygen supply to the muscles. A few quick breaths serve to replenish a seal's oxygen; although a seal's lungs are little bigger than ours the seal can empty and refill them almost completely at each breath instead of only partially as we do. When a seal returns to the surface its heartbeat reverts to a fast rate and moves blood quickly round the body. A seal's physiology is therefore adapted in many ways to making prolonged dives. Some authorities think that it is necessary for seals to spend time basking out of water to compensate for the slow-down of body functions during diving and to 'recharge the batteries' thoroughly before a new diving expedition.

In the natural state seals never seem to suffer from caisson sickness (the bends), a condition that is a threat to all human divers if they ascend from depths of 50 feet or more too quickly. The trouble in the human diver is caused by the pressure on his air supply at considerable depths. Under pressure nitrogen dissolves in the bloodstream. If there is a sudden decrease in pressure — as when a diver comes up to the surface — nitrogen comes out of solution and forms bubbles of gas in the blood vessels. At best this is painful, at worst fatal. The seal avoids this, partly because it takes very little air down when it dives. A seal always exhales as it goes under. This effects neutral buoyancy and expels most of the air from its lungs, so even under pressure (a seal has no fresh supply like a human diver) there is little nitrogen to dissolve in the blood. In addition, the spongy, soft parts of the lungs, containing the alveoli in which gas exchange takes place, are compressed at high pressures; they collapse and most of the residual air in the lung is squeezed into the trachea, which is relatively incompressible but from which no gas can get into the blood. When the seal ascends rapidly there is insufficient nitrogen dissolved in the blood to cause any trouble. There is on record the case of a seal which died from 'bends', but this was one forced to dive experimentally to 900 feet, and it probably did not have a chance to expel air in the normal way. This is probably the exception which proves the rule. Seals are superbly designed diving machines. The Grey Seal has even been seen asleep underwater.

2. Seals and Man

The history of man's relationship with his fellow creatures has been from earliest times one of violence, bloodshed, and destruction. Perhaps no other group of animals has suffered as much as the seals, their mass destruction involving a degree of horror and brutality that is without parallel.

In considering how this has taken place, we must sharply divide the behaviour of human beings indigenous to the homeland of a seal species from mass commercial ventures launched from far distant places. The Eskimos, for example, have always depended upon killing a small number of seals in order to survive. Just as the Lapps used every part of the reindeer in their everyday life, so the Eskimos' existence was entirely bound up with the seal. A seal carcass provided fur clothing, including boots, harpoon lines to kill further seals, dog traces, bags, pouches, skins for covering hulls of boats, bone knives and other primitive instruments — besides the all-important meat as a source of human energy, and the lamp oil to provide light and heat in Arctic conditions. About the only part of the seal that was not used was the liver, which is said to contain such a high vitamin A content as to be toxic to the human system.

The Eskimo killing of seals, though it involved the very high degree of cruelty entailed in harpooning a warm-blooded living creature and playing it as a man may play a fish, was a question of survival only; there was no question of mass financial exploitation. Rudyard Kipling, though the quality of much of his verse may be disputed, possessed to a very high degree the ability to identify himself with the creature, human or animal, that formed his subject, and it is interesting that he did precisely this in the case of the Eskimo who has triumphantly killed his seal and also in the case of a gigantic seal colony almost wiped out by the brutal deputations of sealing vessels coming from far horizons. Here is the Eskimo poem:

ANGUTIVAUN TAINA

Our gloves are stiff with the frozen blood,
Our furs with the drifted snow,
As we come in with the seal — the seal!
In from the edge of the floe.

Au jana! Aua! Oha! Haq!
And the yelping dog-teams go,
And the long whips crack, and the men come back,
Back from the edge of the floe.

We tracked our seal to his secret place,
We heard him scratch below,
We made our mark, and we watched beside,
Out on the edge of the floe.

We raised our lance when he rose to breathe,
We drove it downward — so!
And we played him thus, and we killed him thus,
Out on the edge of the floe.

Our gloves are glued with the frozen blood,
Our eyes with the drifted snow;
But we come back to our wives again,
Back from the edge of the floe!

Au jana! Aua! Oha! Haq!
And the loaded dog teams go,
And the wives can hear their men come back,
Back from the edge of the floe!

The early voyages of discovery of the seventeenth century were the prelude to a policy of massive seal slaughter for monetary gain. The earliest voyagers killed seals out of need, much as the Eskimos always had, to supplement the standard ships' diet of salt meat and biscuits. Gradually, from the realisation of the potentialities in a seal's carcass, a vast industry developed for the sole purpose of hunting seals. These raids may be compared to the extermination of a civilian population by a ferocious army; the seals in their vast colonies had at first no fear of man, regarding him apparently with a mild curiosity, and the slaughter was easy. For the sealers their arrival at the colony was often at the end of an extremely arduous sea voyage, sometimes lasting for months, and the attack upon the colony had a quality of hysteria, in which men lost all humanitarian standards. A great many factors contributed to this. To start with, the killing parties were almost always working against time, and they had been whipped into a sort of frenzy by the captain of the vessel. This was a standard practice, to make certain that the expedition would pay dividends on what was often a huge capital outlay. Even today, that situation is little changed. A young Newfoundland sealer, asked by a friend of mine how he felt about the horrors of his trade replied, 'Well, I don't think I would skin a baby seal alive as some of the others do'. Throughout this book I have tried to be factual, rather than to repeat, even by implication, my own feelings every time the word industry is mentioned in connection with a particular species of seal. Few people who are aware of the facts even in broadest principle can view the sealing industry as anything but a degradation to human nature.

During the nineteenth century the slaughter was so intense, and the seal stocks so depleted, that it became doubtfully profitable to mount any seal hunting expedition on a big scale. This situation only intensified the previous callousness and indifference to animal suffering; to make any profit at all, every thought of either selection or cruelty had to be forgotten absolutely. Many species became practically extinct, and even now some of these exist only in small numbers around remote and uninhabited islands. Rudyard Kipling's second poem, identifying himself with a sacked and plundered seal colony, is certainly a notable example of anthropomorphising, but it was moving to me when I was in the nursery and it is still moving to me now:

LUKANNON

I met my mates in the morning
(And oh but I am old!)
Where roaring on the ledges
The summer ground-swell rolled,
I heard them lift the chorus
That drowned the breakers' song—
The beaches of Lukannon —
Two million voices strong.

The song of pleasant stations
Beside the salt lagoons,
The song of blowing squadrons
That shuffled down the dunes,
The song of midnight dances
That churned the sea to flame —
The beaches of Lukannon —
Before the Sealers came.

I met my mates in the morning
(I'll never meet them more);
They came and went in legions
That darkened all the shore.
And through the foam-flecked offing
As far as voice could reach
We hailed the landing parties
And we sang them up the beach.

The beaches of Lukannon —
The winter-wheat so tall —
The dripping crinkled legions
And the sea-fog drenching all!
The platforms of our playground,
All shining small and worn!
The beaches of Lukannon —
The home where we were born.

I met my mates in the morning,
A broken, scattered band.
Men shoot us in the water
And club us on the land;
Men drive us to the Salt House
Like silly sheep and tame,
And still we sing Lukannon —
Before the Sealers came.

Wheel down, wheel down to southward!
Oh Gooverooska go
And tell the deep sea Viceroys
The story of our woe;
Ere, empty as the shark's egg
The tempest flings ashore,
The beaches of Lukannon
Shall know their sons no more.

Very gradually a certain amount of common sense began to prevail, even though it were a strictly business form of common sense. The sealers began to 'crop' the larger colonies in a more selective and scientific way, so that these succeeded in maintaining their numbers, and in a few cases even began to increase. Quota systems were introduced, and those who over-stepped the limit suffered heavy penalties. More and more species became protected by law, and known breeding grounds were in some cases designated nature reserves or sanctuaries. Many species, however, are still unprotected, and are hunted indiscriminately; the Grey Seal in the Baltic Sea, for example, is gradually being wiped out through persistent and unregulated hunting.

Having presented man's roll as a blood-lusting, money-lusting destroyer of seals, it is reasonable to consider what would happen to a seal colony if it were left strictly alone. Even at some British breeding stations of the Grey Seal there is evidence of overcrowding and high mortality of pups. This may be a good deal worse at some of the huge rookeries of other species and, unwelcome as the truth may be to me and to many, conservation, in the sense of maintaining steady population numbers, may often involve some killing. Whether man is justified in playing God in this way is a question each of us must decide for himself.

These issues are in any case confused by a different aspect — the extraordinary mythology that has grown around seals wherever man has lived in close proximity to them. Seals are mentioned in Greek mythology and in the writings of Homer, Pliny and Plutarch. In every country where man lived close to seals a great wealth of superstition and legend has been handed down from generation to generation, and perhaps to the greatest extent of all in the case of the Grey Seal by the peoples of the Hebrides and the West Coast of Ireland.

In these stories seals take on human form at will, men marry seal women, seals talk and sing, save the lives of fishermen adrift and helpless in high seas, give warning of impending disaster; in short they have been part of an almost religious framework which man constructed from the elements and the animals surrounding him. A great number of these tales, told in the sort of eerie half-light to which they belong, are collected in David Thomson's magnificent book, 'The People of the Sea', subtitled 'A Journey in search of the Seal Legend' and re-issued in 1965. To anyone who has any interest whatsoever in seals this book presents the whole of our dark, mystic involvement with the seal world; it is, so to speak, the other side of the coin from this work, which attempts to present the factual situation.

While many of the legends invest seals with powers of speech and human communication, the belief in their musical abilities belongs probably to a later Celtic fringe of romanticism which crept in during the period corresponding to that in which Sir Edwin Landseer presented the new and strictly romantic image of 'The Monarch of the Glen'. I have before me a newspaper cutting which I believe emanated from 'The Morning Post' during the 1920s, under the paragraph heading 'Seals Sang to Mrs Kennedy-Fraser'.

'Lady Londonderry Recounts Curious Experience

The Music of Lewis

'The Duchess of York has given permission for the dedication to her of the first of a series of books of collected music and songs of the Hebrides by Mr. Duncan Morrison, which is to be published shortly with a foreword and introduction by the Marchioness of Londonderry.

'Lady Londonderry, who has presented Mr Morrison as a pianist and composer to the Queen, the Duchess of York, and other members of the royal family, before whom he has played in private audience, explains:

' "This book of songs from the Isle of Lewis is only the forerunner of other lovely melodies gathered together by Duncan Morrison."

'In another passage Lady Londonderry says — "We may believe it or not, but there is undoubted testimony that the great grey seals of the Atlantic who visit the islands have been heard singing — for no other word applies to their very human voices."

The Response

'Mrs Kennedy-Fraser herself relates how one day, on the island of Barra, she lay on the sand a little distance from the water's edge. She started to sing the seal woman's "Sea Joy" to the seals who were basking in the sunlight on the skerries. Instantly the response began at the southern end of the skerry and a perfect fusillade of answering notes came from seal after seal. Then, after a moment of intense silence, a beautiful solo voice sang a phrase, which Mrs Kennedy-Fraser noted down.

'What is the solution? Is the song which Mrs Kennedy-Fraser sang really a seal song and did the Isles folk learn it from the seals? Mrs Kennedy-Fraser related that in the answering phrase the solo seal sang the interval of an ascending sixth, a favourite melodic practice borrowed from the seals, or did the seals learn it from the Isles folk?'

'Although Mrs Kennedy-Fraser only sang half of the tune to them, it was quite apparent that they knew the whole air, and later on in the same month and year some friends of Mrs Kennedy-Fraser found them singing the second half. She ventures the opinion that singing was perhaps the earliest form of human speech.'

This is but one of many, many examples of a wholly erroneous belief; they start at least as early as 1833 and continue until the present day. In April of last year the following pargraph appeared in the 'News of the World'.

After she had bought the Castle of Mey in Caithness, Queen Elizabeth became an expert at finding the tiny coral-pink cowrie shells known as 'Groatie buckies' in the sand of the lonely shore. She never tires of watching the seals, and was enchanted when, by singing Scottish ballads to them, she brought them closer and closer inshore to listen.

This is a factual misconception which should be cleared up once and for all. Seals have no interest whatever in music, though both in fiction and in some cases of fiction masquerading as fact we read of seals singing, being sung to and charmed, and even playing musical instruments themselves. The belief has grown up from two separate facts, both of which have been misinterpreted. Firstly, seals are by nature intensely inquisitive, and will respond to any unusual sound, provided that it is not a very loud or frightening one, by coming closer to investigate. Secondly, adult Grey Seals, when they are hauled out, produce sounds which may appear to be uncannily like the human voice — though whether or not these represent Mrs Kennedy-Fraser's ascending sixth I cannot say. It is, in any case, time that this particular accretion of mythology were finally prised off from the public's factual image of the seal.

We have two species of seal resident around the coasts of Great Britain, the Grey or Atlantic Seal, and the Common, Harbour or Firth Seal. The Grey Seal is Britain's largest carnivore, and the major part of its world population breeds on or off our shores. Some 30,000 of them haul out to rest regularly on their accustomed rocks and for longer periods to breed and to moult. For the past few years an intense controversy has raged around the official decision to limit their numbers by 'culling' — that is to say the selective killing of a fairly high number of animals every year. The true issues have been obscured by surges of emotional feeling on both sides, and it may be as well to review the facts so that any reader of this book may have enough background knowledge to present his own particular case.

Before 1914 the Grey Seals were in grave danger of extinction. At that time the world population was possibly as low as five hundred individuals. In 1914, largely as a result of the almost obsessional determination of Mr Hesketh Pritchard, the British Government passed a 'Grey Seals Protection Act', which established a closed season from October 1st to December 15th. The seals were thus protected by law during the autumn breeding season when they were most vulnerable to the seal hunters.

As a result of this measure the numbers increased until, by 1927, there were thought to be approximately 8,000. In 1932 a second Grey Seals Protection Act extended the close season by six weeks, from September 1st until December 31st, with special provision for the Hebridean islands of Haskeir. This gave the seals an even better chance of restoring their ranks; but the Government, foreseeing the possible danger of a seal population so high as to threaten coastal fisheries, had empowered the Ministry of Agriculture and Fisheries and the Secretary of State for Scotland to suspend the close season in any one year should it prove necessary.

Complaints about damage to fisheries led to a Conference at Newcastle-upon-Tyne in 1938 and by the mid 1950s the Grey Seal population had increased so much that the Nature Conservancy made grants to natural history societies and university scientists in order to arrive at the true facts.

The damage caused by the seals was reported to be both direct and indirect, and may be briefly summarised as follows:

Direct effects

1. The seals made holes in the nets which allowed the fish to escape.
2. The seals wounded, scarred or totally consumed the fish in the nets,

C

thus reducing very considerably the market value of the fishermen's catches. There were various ways of preventing this. One was to design a new type of seal-proof net; another way was to scare off the seals with rifle shots; a third way, tried out off the Northumberland coast, was to let off underwater explosive charges. In fact nets made of artificial fibres have proved quite effective in reducing the amount of damage done by the seals, but the other methods are too local and too temporary to be of much effect, and gun-fire makes little impression on the seals in bad weather.

Indirect effects

1. The seals do not only eat fish inside fishermen's nets; they also take fish outside the nets in the open sea, not necessarily in the fishing areas. They are therefore held responsible for depleting the stocks of fish in the sea.

2. A parasitic nematode lives in the flesh of the cod-fish, which is one of the ingredients of a Grey Seal's diet. So long as the fish is cooked properly the parasite is perfectly harmless, but in the words of the 1963 *Report on Grey Seals and Fisheries*, it is 'aesthetically undesirable'. The cod-worm passes through part of its life-cycle in the stomach of the Grey and Common Seal. Thus by eating the fish the seals are helping the parasites to complete their life-cycle and multiply their numbers.

The damage caused by Grey Seals to the fishing industry along the east coast of Scotland has been estimated at about £65,000 per year. This estimate has been based upon the average number of fish eaten by a seal and the number of seals seen in the vicinity of the nets.

As a result of these reports the official policy became that of 'culling'; and here we should emphasise again that this word means nothing but selective killing. To implement this policy the 1932 Protection Act was suspended in the Farnes and Orkneys, though 'culling' in the Farnes was halted after three years, owing to the misgivings of the National Trust, which owns the islands.

Having decided upon 'culling', there remained the problem of which section of the seal community to kill — adult bulls, cows, or pups. It was decided that the killing of bulls would be ineffective; bulls are polygamous, and if a harem bull were killed both his territory and his cows would be taken over by another. The killing of cows either before or after the birth of their pups (in which case the pups were killed also) was found by experiment to be impracticable. The third choice was to kill the pups, and this is in fact the present practice. As this takes place after weaning, the lactating cow suffers no ill effects by being deprived of her pup; it is easier to dispose of infant carcases than adult ones; the by-products of pups are readily marketable, for their pelts are of higher quality than the adults'; their oil is used in soap and foodstuff industries, and their meat is turned into dog-food.

The effects of this 'cull' are as yet far from obvious. It is estimated that between 50 and 60 per cent of the pups die in their first year from natural causes, so that it is impossible to say whether or not a pup is being killed which would have died anyway. Because of this, experiments are running parallel, and in some districts both pups and adults are being killed in order to determine the respective effects of the two policies.

It may be as well at this point to review the emotional problems which have caused such an upsurge of public feeling on both sides. Those who object strongly to the killing of the pups feel it to be degrading to the humans concerned to kill in cold blood a helpless and trusting infant of very appealing appearance. There can be few of us who cannot see some strength in this argument. This same group refers very logically to the Hunter Report on Salmon Fishing 1965. This says, in effect, that fishermen should not be killing salmon at sea anyway, and that it would be better to catch salmon by trapping a proportion of them as they come up the rivers to spawn. Salmon return to the same river every year, and by this means the number of salmon caught in a river would be regulated according to its breeding population; killing salmon at sea is largely indiscriminate, and could theoretically result in the extinction of the salmon population of any particular river. If this method were adopted there would be no reason to kill Grey Seals, for they rarely penetrate far into estuaries. Seals would, of course, continue to catch salmon in the sea, but in numbers from which the fishermen would not suffer. Those who would suffer are the owners of sporting salmon rivers, which are of enormous commercial value in the same way as are grouse moors and deer forests.

The arguments on the other side are that such a regulation of salmon fisheries on an entirely new principle would involve the payment of gigantic compensations and an army of white collar workers whose salaries and expenses would become a further charge upon the taxpayers. In short, that there is no case for changing the existing system on account of the emotional reactions of those who do not know the facts.

A true perspective is clearly difficult; but at least nobody can deny that 1,000 years ago there were both many more salmon and many more seals. There were, of course, very much fewer human beings.

3. The Fur Seals

THE NORTHERN FUR SEAL (Frontispiece and Plate 1)   *Callorhinus ursinus*

Distribution and Population

The status of the Northern Fur Seal is an example of the efficacy of scientific methods in cropping and conservation. Alone among the pinnipeds this species has been the subject of controlled hunting and scientific observation for the last half century. The result has been the maintainance of a high population and a lucrative industry. Had sensible control been delayed even for a few years longer it is doubtful whether the species would have survived. As things are, the main colony of Northern Fur Seals, centred on St George and St Paul islands in the Pribilofs, presents in the breeding season the largest aggregation of wild mammals which can be seen in the whole world; larger than the great Caribou herds in North America, larger than any of the remaining herds of African game. This colony is estimated to contain one and a half million Fur Seals, and half a million pups are born every year. Besides the Pribilof colony, Northern Fur Seals are found on the Commander Islands and on Robben Island in the Sea of Okhotsk. These two colonies contain a further 200,000 or more individuals. On the Kurile Islands, which the Northern Fur Seals once inhabited, some small groups have been reported in recent years, and recolonisation may be already underway. The total population of the Northern Fur Seal is probably in the region of two million.

Appearance and description

An adult female is about 5 feet long and weighs up to 130 pounds. The males are about 7 feet long when fully grown. It is not so much their greater length which distinguishes the males from the females but their huge bulk, for a big male may weigh nearly 6 hundredweight. The sexes also differ in colour. The males have dark brown fur all over the body, except for the mane, which has a greyish tinge. The females are slate grey above and a lighter reddish-grey below. There is a light patch on the chest of both sexes. If the outer hairs are removed the chestnut-coloured underfur is revealed. Albinos have occasionally been found.

Habitat and habits

The Northern Fur Seal digests its food before returning to land, and examination of the specimens killed ashore thus reveals very little about diet. Investigation of habits at sea has shown, however, that the Fur Seal spends most of the day sleeping, and feeds either at night or at dawn and dusk. Most of the characteristic items of diet — squids, herring and pollack — are taken in superficial waters; but the species has been found 40 fathoms below the surface, and fish from the stomachs of the seals (such as 'seal-fish', *Bathylagus callorhinus*) show that these dives are food-seeking expeditions. The Fur Seal's tastes appear catholic, and cod, lampreys, lantern-fish and rock-fish are recorded. A big bull feeding at sea may eat as much as 40 pounds of fish in a day, cows a smaller amount proportionate to their lesser bulk.

Although ill-adapted to life on terra firma, Pribilof Fur Seals contrive quite long journeys over land, but their laborious progress, with frequent rests, contrasts sharply with their ease and agility in the water. They are highly gregarious and very noisy. Their voices — loud coughs, roars, barks, and bleating sounds — seems to convey their emotional state to their fellows.

The only enemies of a grown Fur Seal are man and the formidable Killer Whale. A Killer Whale's appetite is large, and one specimen's stomach was found to contain twenty-four Fur Seals.

Seasonal movements

The Northern Fur Seal is renowned for its seasonal migrations. As the northern winter begins, the seals leave their rookery haunts and move southwards. Most of the Pribilof seals move down the west coast of America, while those from Commander and Robben travel down the coast of Japan. Some cross the Pacific and travel down the opposite coast. In the western Pacific they migrate as far south as Tokyo, and in the east as far as San Diego. Fur Seals have occasionally been seen migrating northwards from the Pribilofs instead of southwards, but these were juveniles, apparently having the right idea but no sense of direction. The adult females are first to leave the rookeries. They start to move south in late September and early October, and are followed in November by the bulls and young. The bulls do not usually venture far, and most of them can be found just south of the Aleutian Islands. The females and the young animals go much further afield and in December some can be found as far south as San Francisco. As the seals travel alone or in small groups of perhaps half a dozen, the herds become widely scattered, and by the New Year individuals may be found as far apart as San Diego and the Aleutians. Migrating seals stay about 50 miles offshore unless they are drawn in closer by large schools of herring. They remain widely dispersed until April, when they begin the return journey. Most of the adults are back at the rookeries by June, but young seals are still at sea. In the western Pacific the return is a little later.

The seals return to the same rookery year after year, and it remains a mystery how they find their way back, especially when, as in the case of adult females, they may have travelled thousands of miles from their birthplace.

Reproduction

The bulls establish their territories on arrival at the rookery, and thereafter rarely fight over them. A bull seeing another approaching his territory will advance threateningly to his frontier zone, but before either reaches the boundary they both drop on to their bellies and slither forward until their mouths touch. Neither tries to cross the boundary and peace is maintained. A newcomer to a fully-occupied beach is met with less tolerance, and a real fight may ensue.

The females do not arrive at the rookeries until the bulls have established territories for their harems, which may consist of up to fifty cows. Mating lasts over the next two months, accompanied by constant threatening between the harem bulls. The bachelor bulls remain inland from the breeding beaches, waiting hopefully for stray females. Towards the end of the breeding season some of them mate with the virgin females, who until then have stayed offshore.

By the end of the season the harem bulls have become so thin and weak that they can hardly make their way back to the sea. Delayed implantation occurs in this species, and the blastocyst does not become embedded in the wall of the womb until three-and-a-half to four months after conception.

Birth to maturity

The cows give birth a few days after they have come ashore, the pupping season reaching its height between June 20th and July 20th. The new-born pups are about two feet long and weigh about 12 pounds. A normal delivery takes about 10 minutes, the pup being born head first. When the pup is about 8 weeks old its coarse black coat is replaced by one which is steely grey above and creamy white below. The young seal does not acquire the darker adult coat until it is some two years old.

The mother is very attentive towards the pup for the first few days after birth, keeping it away from danger and threatening other seals that approach too close; but her interest soon wanes and the maternal function is restricted to occasional suckling. The pups are prepared to suckle from any cow, but a mother will feed only her own pup, which she distinguishes without difficulty, smelling its nose to make sure that it is her own before feeding it.

About two weeks after birth the females go back to the sea, returning to their pups for one day in the week. The cows give suck for three months; at the end of this period the pups are taking about a gallon of milk at each feed. Although the young are capable of swimming at birth, they rarely enter the water until they are a month old. They gather in groups or 'pods' in parts of the rookery where they are not likely to be disturbed, and spend their time with their own age group, playing, sleeping or sometimes wandering around the rookery.

Although the cows are sexually mature at 3 years of age, and may bear pups at 4, the first pup is not usually carried until the female is 5 or 6. Their breeding life is long and they have been known to pup at the age of 21. The bulls do not achieve harem bull status until they are at least 12 years old, although they are sexually mature at 5 or 6, and begin to copulate at 8. The Northern Fur Seal is known to achieve at least 30 years of age, but harem status is not retained beyond the age of 20. Marked seals have been seen on Pribilof over a period of twenty-six years.

The species in relation to man

Northern Fur Seals have been hunted commercially since the time of their discovery on the Pribilof Islands. The islands were discovered in 1786 by Gerassim Pribilof, a Russian explorer and fur trader, who must have been elated to find such a rich new source of furs. In the next eighty years the Russians harvested nearly two and a half million seal skins, but this slaughter was indiscriminate, and twice during the period, once in 1806 and again in 1834, the industry came to a halt for lack of seals. Eventually the Russians appreciated the principle of conservation, and when sealing was resumed only bulls were killed, which has remained standard practice on the Pribilofs to this day.

The United States bought Alaska from Russia, and in 1870 the Alaska Commercial Company took control of sealing in the Pribilofs, fixing an annual quota of 100,000. This figure was easy to achieve during the first few seasons, but in 1879 a new development was very nearly fatal to the Pribilof seals. In that year five sealing schooners sailed to poach seals at sea, where there were no legal restrictions on numbers. This slaughter proved extremely profitable, and a large industry developed from it. By 1883 the Alaska Commercial Company was unable to reach its quota, and by 1890 the shore sealing industry had virtually collapsed due to the toll taken at sea. By this time, however, the Company had taken two million skins, and the tax and royalties paid on these alone very nearly repaid the U.S. Government for the purchase of Alaska.

Killing Fur Seals at sea was a disastrously wasteful process, as for every seal taken three or four were lost, sinking before they were recovered. It was also indiscriminate; it is very difficult to distinguish cows from bulls in the water, and about 60 per cent of the animals recovered proved to be cows.

This pelagic sealing became a source of dispute between the sealing nations, but eventually in 1911 a treaty was concluded which banned the practice. In compensation, those nations whose ships had participated received a share in the catch of the shore-killed animals. Under the treaty the U.S.A. and Russia both gave Japan and Great Britain (and now Canada) 15 per cent of their kill and Japan gave the other nations 10 per cent of hers. Under these new regulations the breeding population on the Pribilofs increased remarkably. In 1943, for the first time since 1889, the number of skins collected exceeded 100,000.

At present, between 60,000 and 70,000 seals are taken commercially each year, but to maintain the structure and population these are all bachelor bulls. They have to be of a certain length, and the majority (two-thirds) are three-year-olds, the remainder being four-year-olds with a few five- or six-year-olds.

The bachelor bulls are easy to take, as they normally remain separate from the main herd, and may be easily driven on to suitable beaches. Those that are not of the minimum size are allowed to return to the rookery, while the remainder are killed and skinned. The skins are washed, de-blubbered, salted and packed in barrels before being sent to St Louis in Missouri for processing. The Japanese and Canadian quotas are despatched unprocessed.

Processing involves, firstly, the removing of the guard hairs by cutting away the underlying layers of skin in which they are embedded. Pulling away these hairs reveals the shorter and less deeply rooted underfur, which is straightened, dyed, and dressed to make it supple. The whole process takes three months. The high quality of the Pribilof skins makes them especially suitable for fur coats.

Although fishermen complain of the damage done to their nets, and the losses to their salmon catches, the damage attributable to the Northern Fur Seal is slight, and any inconvenience to the fishermen is more than outweighed by the value of fur and by-products.

The species in captivity

Very few specimens of the Northern Fur Seal have been kept in captivity. The Aquarium at the Bureau of Fisheries in Washington received a pair in 1909, one of which lived nine years in captivity, apparently a record for this species. San Diego Zoo has also kept them and trained them, and they have been found to be almost as good performers as the Californian Sealion.

THE SOUTH AMERICAN OR   *Arctocephalus australis*
SOUTHERN FUR SEAL (Plate 1)

Distribution and population

Three sub-species are recognised, due mainly to skull differences.

A. australis gracilis inhabits the coasts and islands from southern Brazil around Cape Horn to southern Peru. This form is fairly common off the coasts of Chile, and occasionally off Peru. Another large population is found on Uruguayan islands, where there are estimated to be about 70,000 individuals, over 50,000 of which are on the Isla de Lobos (called after *Lobo marino* — Sea wolf).

A. australis australis is found on the Falkland Islands, where the population is estimated at 20,000.

A. australis galapagoensis is the Galapagos Fur Seal and at present appears to be restricted to Tower and James Islands, although some may be present on Narborough and Albemarle Islands. The population of Galapagos Fur Seals is thought to be increasing, but is little more than 2,000.

The total population of the South American Fur Seal is therefore approximately 100,000.

Appearance and description

The adult males are up to 6 feet in length, except the Galapagos sub-species, which are a little smaller (up to 5 feet), and weigh up to 300 pounds. The females are smaller, about 4 feet 6 inches in length and weighing only 90 pounds. The males are blackish grey, but the females appear to vary; the typical form is white-tipped grey on the neck and along the back, and yellowish on the underside of the body.

Habitat and habits

The distribution of the Southern Fur Seal is approximately that of the Southern Sealion, and they intermingle. Except during the breeding seasons the two species tolerate each other, but fights break out during the rut, and it is usually the Fur Seal that wins. Fur Seals and Sealions sometimes breed on the same beach, but the breeding season of the Sealion is later in the year than that of the Fur Seal. There is a tendency for the two species to occupy different parts of the coasts on which they occur, as the Fur Seal prefers rocky shores and the Sealion flat sandy beaches.

The diet of the Fur Seal probably consists mainly of fish, crustaceans, and squids, but little except stones has been found in the stomachs of those animals examined. Stomach ulcers have been noted. Their enemies are man, Killer Whales and sharks, and a shark has been found with five young Fur Seals in its stomach.

Seasonal movements

Apart from the Falkland Island herds there is no true migration in this group. During the winter and again during the spring there is some movement between the Uruguayan islands, but no true migration. The Lobos seals are found on the island all the year round. The Falkland Island population, however, moves northwards during the winter to the Uruguayan islands, and southwards again in the following spring.

Reproduction

During November the harem bulls stake out their territories in preparation for the arrival of the cows at the end of the month. When the cows arrive bulls form harems of from three to five. The pups are born soon after the arrival of their mothers, who are served within a few days of pupping. The breeding season continues until the beginning of January, when the harems begin to disintegrate. The length of delayed implantation is not known with certainty, but it is thought that the blastocyst implants in the wall of the womb some time between April and July.

For about six months the cows feed their pups regularly, and some are suckled for as much as a year, but in general the pups are fed less often after the July following their birth.

The species in relation to man

In commercial value the Southern Fur Seal skins stand about midway between the skins of the Pribilof and Cape Fur Seals. The annual haul of skins is about 4,500, of which 80 per cent come from the Isla de Lobos. One-and-a half to two-year-old males form the majority of the kill. The pelts are treated in much the same way as those of the Pribilof seals. Uruguay has only a small industry, but is the only South American country exploiting the Fur Seals.

THE PHILIPPI OR GUADALUPE FUR SEAL (Plate 1)   *Arctocephalus philippii*

Distribution and population

The story of the Philippi Fur Seal is a shocking indictment of the short-sightedness of nineteenth century sealers, who not only robbed themselves of a living but very nearly robbed the world of a species of animal as well. Nobody knows exactly how many Philippi Fur Seals were living at the time of their discovery, but there must have been millions. Today there are probably less than five hundred, and the survival of even this number is little short of miraculous. There used to be two major population centres, one in the Juan Fernandez Islands off the Chilean coast, and the other around Guadalupe (and perhaps some of the other islands) off southern California. No undoubted Philippi Fur Seals have been recorded between these two groups of islands, which are several thousand miles apart, and on the basis of their geographical separation, and some minor skull characters, some authorities give the two races sub-specific status. The Juan Fernandez Fur Seal (*A.p. philippii*) is now extinct and all the surviving Philippi Fur Seals are of the northern race (*A.p. townsendi*), which is, incidentally, the only member of the *Arctocephalus* genus to occur north of the equator.

Appearance and description

There are few observations on the Guadalupe Fur Seal, and little is known of its habits. Males grow up to 6 feet in length, the females a little smaller. Most of the body has dark grey fur, but the sides of the snout are rufous with light coloured whiskers.

Reproduction

Harems are probably formed in the usual way, and the pups born in the early summer. Pups have been seen suckling in October, but apart from this observation the breeding habits remain a mystery.

The species in relation to man

During the eighteenth century large numbers of Fur Seals were to be found on practically all the islands off the Pacific coast of America from what is now San Francisco southwards to Cape Horn. Carteret, on a voyage round the world in 1767 visited the island of Masafuera (one of the Juan Fernandez group) and found that 'the seals were so numerous that I verily think that if many thousands of them were killed in a night they would not be missed in the morning: we were obliged to kill great numbers of them as, when we walked the shore, they were continually running against us, making at the same time a most horrible noise. These animals yield excellent train oil, and their hearts and plucks are very good eating, being in taste something like those of a hog, and their skins are covered with the finest fur I ever saw of the kind.' The Fur Seals he saw were almost undoubtedly the Juan Fernandez race of the Philippi Fur Seal. 'Train oil' was not for lubricating locomotives, but was a term applied to oil prepared by boiling blubber from whales or seals. Such oil was put to a variety of uses, including lamp fuel, a soft soap with tallow, and waterproofing clothing.

As long as only occasional visits were paid to the islands by voyagers like Carteret the seals as a species were in no danger of extinction, but in the nineteenth century a great sealing industry grew up around these eastern Pacific islands. The slaughter of Fur Seals was immense. In a seven year period on Masafuera three million skins were taken, and further north near California some two or three thousand skins a week were taken throughout the breeding season. Altogether several thousand men were employed in the trade, but it seems that their capacity for slaughter was in inverse proportion to their common sense and powers of observation. They failed to understand that their indiscriminate killing was pushing the breeding rookeries beyond the point of no return. Farmed sensibly by taking only idle bulls, the vast Fur Seal colonies could have provided many thousands of skins annually without detriment to the species. Exploited without foresight, by landing and massacring as many Fur Seals as possible regardless of age or sex, the rookeries were doomed. By the end of the nineteenth century sealing in this part of the world could no longer show a profit. The sealers had wiped out their livelihood and nearly all the seals; and besides being wasteful they were also unobservant. To them all

Fur Seals were the same, and so it was not until 1866, when a zoologist named Peters compared the skulls and skins from Juan Fernandez and from the South American mainland, that the two distinct species were recognised. The Juan Fernandez skins were collected on the islands in 1864 by a man named Philippi, and the species was named after him, but by that time the Juan Fernandez Fur Seal was almost extinct.

Not until 1892 was a Guadalupe Fur Seal skin collected, examined, and shown to be different from the Galapagos Fur Seal (*A. australis*) but very similar to the Juan Fernandez Fur Seal, with which it is now included as a single species. Why the two populations were so far apart, sandwiching another species between them, is not understood; perhaps at one time their range was continuous. It is unlikely that two species of similar ecology ever shared the Galapagos Islands, but there is no evidence that one replaced the other.

Nothing has been heard of the Juan Fernandez Fur Seal for more than 60 years; the last reliable reports were in the 1880s, though a batch of 50 Fur Seal skins, said to come from the islands, were sold in London at the turn of the century. The Guadalupe Fur Seal, too, was believed extinct, but in the 1920s a small group was discovered. The treatment received by this pathetic remnant was no better than that meted out to their teeming forebears. This was in 1926, when two fishermen named Clover and, appropriately, Fisher, reported to Dr Wedgeworth, founder of San Diego Zoological Society, that they had seen what they thought were Fur Seals on Guadalupe. Excited by the prospect of re-discovering a species thought to be extinct Wedgeworth engaged Clover to catch a specimen. To his delight Clover was successful and caught two bulls, which were sent to San Diego Zoo in 1928, where they were identified as true Philippi Fur Seals. A little later Clover quarrelled with Wedgeworth, and in a fit of temper stormed off to Guadalupe, threatening to kill the whole herd on the island. This he apparently did. He took the skins to Panama to sell, and there he was killed in a bar-room fight.

An expedition sailed to where the herd had been reported but there were no seals there, and it was concluded that this time the Fur Seals were really extinct, with the exception of the San Diego bulls which could never breed. However, a few were seen by naturalists before the Second World War, and then in 1949 a single bull was observed among a herd of sealions on San Nicholas, off Los Angeles. At last, in 1954, a true colony was found on Guadalupe, living in a cave. Although there are only three or four hundred animals in the herd it seems that they breed regularly in this hiding place, and if they are left unmolested there is every hope that the population may expand and perhaps even colonise some of the former breeding sites.

THE SOUTH AFRICAN OR   *Arctocephalus pusillus*
CAPE FUR SEAL (Plate 2)

Distribution and population

Arctocephalus pusillus is one of the commonest and most distinct of the Fur Seals. It inhabits the rocks and islands off the coasts of South West Africa and Cape Province, and the estimated population is about 500,000.

Appearance and description

The adult males are very large. They reach 9 feet in length, and weigh, depending on the time of year, between 450 and 700 pounds. The females grow up to 6 feet and weigh between 200 and 250 pounds. The males have a coarse coat of dark blackish-grey fur which tends to be lighter under the body, whereas the females are an all-over brownish-grey. Colour differences between individuals are not as a rule marked, though russet coloured males have been reported. The muzzle bears about thirty moustachial bristles which are short and black in the pups but gradually turn lighter, and in the adults are white. To estimate the age of the adults is not easy, as the teeth do not show consistent ringing (cf. the Californian Sealion) and size is not a reliable indication of age.

Habitat and habits

These seals spend much time in the water, and on leaving a rookery they reach deep water within a few hours. The bulls stay away from the rookeries for between 22 and 34 weeks of the year, the females for between 12 to 35 weeks, yearlings for only a few weeks, and the sub-adults for about 38 weeks. They can keep pace with a boat travelling at about 8 knots, but only over short distances. They swim just below the surface, breaking it only to breathe and to control their general direction of movement. Sometimes they swim in porpoise fashion, which does not gain them extra speed but enables them to detect pursuers, and to manoeuvre towards a rookery.

Very little disease has been found in the rookeries, and ailing individuals are assumed to haul out elsewhere. Parasites are numerous in the skin of all the seals, especially of the older specimens, but these infestations do not appear to cause inconvenience.

During the period between breeding seasons the bulls spend 2 to 3 weeks in each month on feeding expeditions. The cows spend a little more time on land in order to feed their pups, but they too are away at sea feeding for a week or two every month. Feeding is entirely at sea, and the diet consists mainly of pilchards and squids, although other fish, rock lobsters, and small crustaceans are also acceptable. Stones have been found in the stomachs of seals of all ages, and the large quantities found in the older pups may compensate for the lack of food in the stomach during the absence of the mothers.

The adult seals hunt singly, or in groups of two or three, unless a shoal of fish draws a number of them to the area. Small fish they swallow whole, but larger ones they bring to the surface and break up. They fish near to the surface and seldom dive to more than 150 feet. While feeding at sea they take frequent rests between meals; and, as digestion is slow, a long rest ashore is needed to clear the alimentary canal. The maximum amount of food which may be taken by an adult at one meal is 25 pounds of fish or 30 pounds of squids. The normal intake is well below the maximum, being only 3 or 4 pounds per meal.

Seasonal movements

The species does not migrate but seals range over a wide area while feeding. Tagged pups have been found 800 miles north of their birthplace at the end of their first year. The Cape Fur Seal wanders far afield and hauls out at strange rookeries, but always returns to its birthplace to breed, and never moves more than 100 miles from land.

The effect of the cold Benguela current extends over the whole range of the species, and the animals have, therefore, no real need to change their position according to the season.

D

Reproduction

In November the bulls arrive at the rookeries fresh from winter feeding and begin to establish their territories. There is very little fighting, but much threatening. (When sealing operations interfere with the natural dominance pattern fierce and desperate fighting breaks out between males.) The cows arrive shortly after the bulls and copulation takes place on land and in the water, but the blastocyst does not implant until the following April or May. Twin blastocysts and foetuses occur but only rarely are twin pups successfully born.

The adult harem bulls patrol their territories and prevent serious fights breaking out between cows over pups, but they do not appear to prevent cows in their harems moving into another territory, and some cows actively seek other bulls. Defence of territory tends to decrease soon after the birth of the pups.

Birth to maturity

The pups are born at the end of November and beginning of December and are about 2 feet 6 inches in length and weigh about 14 pounds. They are covered in a velvety coat of short, black, curly hairs which is moulted after 4 or 5 months. The new coat is olive grey with some black hairs tipped with white, and a thick brown underfur. A year later the fur moults again and gives place to a silvery grey coat, which fades during the following summer to a dark colour above and a lighter shade below. Each of these two moults takes about 6 weeks.

The newly born pup starts suckling within an hour of being born, and the milk contains 18.6 per cent fat and 10 per cent protein. The fat content is not as high as that of pinnipeds or cetaceans which live in colder regions.

The cow stays with her pup for about a week and then returns to the sea for a few days before coming back to give suck. Her absences gradually lengthen until by the second month she may stay away for as long as 2 weeks at a time. By the time the pup is 5 months old it has started to supplement its milk diet with some fish and crustaceans, although much of what it ingests is inedible. By October, almost 12 months after birth, the pups are weaned, able to catch their own food and to survive independently of their mothers. At birth the youngster has a set of milk teeth which are lost at the time of change to solid diet. If a pup of the succeeding year dies, the one-year-old may continue suckling.

Towards the end of the first year the pup has added squids to its diet. The fluid contained in their ink sacs, which may be used as writing ink, is a powerful stain and discolours the yearling's teeth to brown or black. The permanent teeth, which start to grow after the milk teeth have been lost, are slow in assuming the adult form, and the canines do not grow above the height of the incisors until the second year.

The young pup has a short face, but as it grows the skull length increases faster than the width, and the rounded features of the pup skull take on the more rugged appearance of the adult. At birth the pup has a whitish nose, and also light coloured soles to the flippers, but the colour darkens and turns black after a few days. Albinos are not recorded, but cases of partial albinism with white moustachial bristles have been observed. Each flipper bears five claws, the outer two being shorter than the inner three. The claws are three-quarters of an inch long at birth but as the pup grows older they are gradually worn down through grooming.

The male pups are generally the more active and playful; they grow much faster, and may double their weight by the second month. By April male pups may weigh over 50 pounds and females over 38 pounds.

The young seals seldom wander far from the rookery in the first year, and suckle and sleep alongside the cows in the early morning and late evening. By the second year they become much more independent. Cows first mate when they are nearly 2 years old, somewhat earlier in the year than their elders, and their gestation period may be 2 to 3 months longer than normal. The males are sexually, but not physically, mature in their third year and, although they may then mate with virgin cows, it is some years before they achieve the status of harem bulls.

The species in relation to man

The hunting of the South African Fur Seal began with the discovery of the Cape, but the seals were soon over-exploited and the industry collapsed. In the eighteenth century the cycle was repeated. In the present century the South African Government took control of commercial sealing, but it was not until

1946 that biological research led to the selection of seals which could be killed and the stabilisation of population figures.

Present regulations stipulate limited periods in the summer and winter when seals may be taken. During the South African summer (between late October and the first week of December) 6,000 surplus bulls are killed in selected rookeries. The majority of these pelts are scarred and in poor condition, and the seals are killed mainly for their blubber. Summer sealing was intended to apply only to idle bulls, but the distinction has been found difficult, and stampedes have led to the crushing of younger animals. The present trend is to restrict the summer activities still further, and to concentrate on the winter period.

The winter season lasts from July to early September, and concentrates upon pups between 7 and 10 months old. At this age the pelt is at its best quality, long, well-textured, and unscarred, and the blubber is thick. These winter operations account for about 30,000 yearlings of both sexes.

The species in captivity

The Cape Fur Seal thrives in captivity on a diet of 5 to 15 pounds of fish a day, and has lived to 20 years of age under sheltered conditions. A pair kept by the Zoological Society of London lived to the ages of 20 and 12½ years respectively.

THE AUSTRALIAN FUR SEAL (Plate 2)   *Arctocephalus doriferus*

Distribution and population

The Australian Fur Seal is often confused with the Sealion and the larger Tasmanian Fur Seal where the species overlap in the Bass Strait, and for this reason many of the references to these animals in older books cannot be relied upon. The range of the *Arctocephalus doriferus* is from Eclipse Island in Western Australia to Kangaroo Island in South Australia. Authorities are still by no means unanimous in their recognition of the species and it is not surprising that information is scanty and original observations few and far between.

Due also to confusion of identity, population figures are unknown, but numbers are thought to be increasing over a large part of the range.

Appearance and description

The males grow up to 6 feet in length and are greyish-brown above and lighter below. The females reach 5 feet in length, with coloration the same as that of the males.

Reproduction

The individuals congregate in the rookeries towards the end of October and normal harem formation is believed to be the rule. The pups are born at the end of December.

The species in relation to man

The killing of the Australian Fur Seal is permitted under licence only.

THE TASMANIAN FUR SEAL   *Arctocephalus tasmanicus*

Distribution and population

This species, one of the larger Fur Seals, is found on suitably rocky parts of the Tasmanian coast, on islands in the Bass Strait, and around the shores of New South Wales and Victoria on the mainland of Australia. The total population is at least 12,000, some 5,000 of which colonise Seal Rocks off Phillip Island, and a further 5,000 inhabit Lady Julia Percy Island. Smaller colonies occur on the Skerries (800) and on Anser and Glennie Islands (1,200).

Appearance and description

The males may reach 8 feet in length, and the females 5 feet. The pelt is grey above and brown below.

Habitat and habits

These seals feed in the water, and from examinations of stomach contents their food appears to consist mainly of crayfish, squids and barracouta, although other fish have been noted.

Reproduction

The adults gather in the rookeries around the coasts during October and November and each bull forms a harem of six or seven cows.

Birth to maturity

The pups are born between mid-November and mid-December, with a rich chocolate-coloured coat. They are suckled for about six months.

The species in relation to man

The areas which the species inhabits are used for commercial fishing, and the seals have a reputation for eating marketable fish and for destroying nets, though this has not been substantiated. The barracouta, which form part of the Fur Seal diet, are also an important food fish for humans, and the fishing industry is apprehensive about the effects of seals on stocks, but barracouta are still plentiful and no decline in their numbers is apparent. The seals are protected, and the only time they may be killed without licence is when they are found interfering with nets.

THE NEW ZEALAND FUR SEAL (Plate 2)   *Arctocephalus forsteri*

Distribution and population

The New Zealand Fur Seal is found on the mainland of New Zealand and on islands to the south as far as Macquarie Island. Macquarie was once an important breeding station, and thousands of skins were taken annually for a few years after the discovery of the island in 1810. The species was not seen again on the island until 1955, and the seals now appear to be re-establishing themselves. They occupy their chosen coasts for about nine months of the year, and leave only to feed.

The total population was recently believed to be less than 50,000, but there has been a rapid increase over the last few years, and the number may in fact have doubled.

Appearance and description

The New Zealand Fur Seal is one of the less bulky of the fur seals, and although the males may be 7 feet long they seldom weigh as much as 300 pounds. There is less disparity of size between the sexes than in most fur seals, but the females are slightly shorter. Both sexes are dark grey above and brown below.

Habitat and habits

Their food consists to a large extent of squids, which form about 50 per cent of their diet, the rest being composed of large crustaceans, and non-commercial fish of the region, such as Snake-Mackerels and Nibblers. They also take Shags and Penguins, which they skin as do Leopard Seals.

Reproduction

Each bull forms a harem of up to ten cows, and the males take up their positions about a fortnight before the pups are born. Pupping begins early in December, and the bulls guard their females until the end of the season in the middle of February.

Birth to maturity

The pups when born are black or silver grey and are about 18 inches long. The cow suckles her pup for about eight months.

The species in relation to man

A sealing industry had been established by the early nineteenth century but hunting was so intense that by 1840 it was no longer profitable. In 1814/15,

400,000 skins were taken from the Antipodes Islands but, due to the necessary haste, many were imperfectly cured. The ship *Pegasus* sailed for Britain with a cargo of 100,000 skins; but on arrival in London it was found that the skins had heated during the voyage, and had to be dug out of the holds and sold as manure, a hundred thousand lives taken to no purpose.

The species was once plentiful on the South Island of New Zealand, as is shown by the large numbers of bones identified among the refuse dumps of Maori settlements a few centuries old. To these people the Fur Seal must have been a common food.

At the time of Cook's second voyage round the world the Fur Seals were still numerous, and according to Forster's account of the voyage many were killed by the crew.

The species has been protected by the New Zealand Government for the past fifty years, with occasional open seasons. Eleven thousand males, females and pups were killed during the late 1940s when traders managed to obtain licences, but this caused such a public outcry that the number of licences was thereafter drastically curtailed. It has been very difficult to ascertain the population increase owing to this protection, but it is certainly significant.

THE KERGUELEN FUR SEAL (Plate 2)   *Arctocephalus tropicalis*

Distribution and population

Two sub-species are recognised, separated geographically by the Antarctic Convergence (the point at which the cold water from the Antarctic sinks under the warmer water of the Pacific and Atlantic Oceans).

Arctocephalus tropicalis tropicalis is found from St Paul and Amsterdam Islands in the Indian Ocean to Tristan da Cunha and Gough Islands in the Atlantic Ocean.

Arctocephalus tropicalis gazella occurs from the Kerguelen Islands in the Indian Ocean to South Georgia, South Orkney, and South Shetland, south east of Cape Horn.

The total population of the northern sub-species is unknown, but it has been estimated that some 12,000 Fur Seals inhabit Gough Island. Individuals of the southern form, *A.t. gazella*, are distributed over a wide area, and here again the population figures are unknown. A few individuals were seen early in the twentieth century, but the sub-species was thought to be extinct until in 1933 a small colony was found on Bird Island off the north west tip of South Georgia. By 1936 this colony numbered about 13,000 and by 1962 it was estimated at some 33,000 excluding the pups. Other colonies have been found on South Orkney, South Sandwich, and South Shetland, presumably offshoots of the original colony on Bird Island.

The total population of the southern sub-species is therefore not less than 40,000, and may be very much greater.

Appearance and description

Morphologically, the sub-species differ only slightly. The males of the sub-species *A.t. tropicalis* are dark grey above, with the throat, face and chest bright yellow, and stomach brown. The head bears a patch of darker fur extending back from between the eyes to a point level with the ears. Males over the age of 5 develop a distinct crest of longer hairs on top of their heads. The females of this sub-species resemble the males in colour, except that the yellow chest is duller.

Males of the sub-species *A.t. gazella* are olive-grey to silvery colour dorsally, with a brownish belly, and a dark yoke over the middle. The guard hairs of the neck and shoulders are longer and grow haphazardly, forming a dense mane. As with the other sub-species, a crest is present on the head of those males over the age of 5. Female coloration is similar, but mane and yoke are absent, and the throat and chest are creamy.

Males of both forms weigh up to 400 pounds and reach 5 to 6 feet in length. The females are smaller, up to 4 feet 6 inches in length, and weighing a maximum of 110 pounds.

A.t. gazella is the only large stock of the genus *Arctocephalus* which has been studied in the natural state, and it has been possible to observe colonies unaffected by any recent depredation.

Habitat and habits

These seals favour a coastline where there are a number of rocky coves with broad sandy beaches sheltered by the mainland. They leave these beaches for frequent feeding expeditions, but first wash off all the collected dirt and grime from their coats. The staple food is the surface dwelling crustacean *Euphausia superba*, the krill, and *A.t. gazella* appears to depend almost exclusively on this source. This has led to the molar teeth being reduced in size compared with other Fur Seals, including *A.t. tropicalis* which is a fairly catholic feeder. Both forms, however, are known sometimes to eat fish, Gentoo Penguins, and squids, as well as the crustaceans.

Chief enemies are Killer Whales, Leopard Seals, and, in the warmer waters, sharks. The toll levied by these predators is, however, slight, and deaths due to parturition, or fighting between bulls, outnumber any others.

Seasonal movements

Movement at sea has been imperfectly defined, but the southern form is believed to move northwards in the winter to maintain contact with the krill pastures which were on the Antarctic Convergence in summer.

The younger animals tend to wander over a large area, and individuals are occasionally seen on the coast of the South Island of New Zealand, and even with New Zealand Fur Seals (*A. forsteri*) on Macquarie Island.

Reproduction

The bulls arrive at the rookeries fresh from winter feeding at sea, and take up their territories along the water's edge. They are extremely pugnacious, and establish their territories with fierce fighting. Territorial boundaries are marked by some natural feature of the terrain, such as tussocks of grass and lines of rocks; these markers do not form any true obstacles, but serve to remind each bull that on crossing the line they are leaving their own territory and entering that of another. If a bull does stray into the territory of another, a fight is inevitable, the bulls facing each other and slashing at their opponent's throat and chest with their open mouths. The thick skin and dense mane around the throat and chest has a protective function, but despite this severe wounds are not rare, and by the end of the breeding season the coat around the throat and chest of many of the bulls is matted with dry blood and dirt. Fighting is usually inconclusive, both bulls breaking off and retreating into their own territory, only to return and start afresh. Possession is nine points of the law amongst Fur Seals and an occupying bull can drive away much larger intruders.

Latecomers to the rookery are at a distinct disadvantage, for the earlier arrivals have already marked out their territories. As soon as the newcomer hauls ashore he finds himself in another bull's territory, and the owner attacks him fiercely. The intruder then has a choice, either to return to the water or to make a mad dash through the rookery to some point inland of the harem bulls.

By the end of November a definite pattern has emerged at the rookery. The dominant bulls are spaced along the water's edge, others a little to landward, and still more further inland at the high tide line. A fourth group mark the periphery of the rookery, and a fifth, mainly four and five-year-old males, roam the shallow waters just off the shore.

The cows begin to arrive at the rookeries in the second week of November, and the main body arrives in December. There is no active collection of cows for the harems. If a cow is not happy in one harem she moves off to another, and the bull does not and cannot prevent her from doing so. The bulls are more concerned with the maintenance of their territories than with competition for cows. When the rookery settles down the majority of the cows are in harems along the shore. Harem size varies from one to twenty cows per bull, with an average of nine. Many bulls, mainly sub-adults, fail to get a cow at all.

Mating begins a week or so after the cows give birth. After having been served, the cows leave the beach and enter the water, where they are again served by the aquatic bulls. The vast majority of copulations take place in the water, but many of these do not give rise to fertilisation. Length of delay in implantation has not been established, but the active pregnancy is about nine months.

Birth to maturity

The pups are born between two and four days after the arrival of the cows at the rookery. The birth is rapid, and the pup is shot out of the body of the female by violent muscular contractions of the womb. When the pup first appears the cow may pull at it with her teeth to ease delivery, and once it is born she nibbles at the forward end of the pup to remove the foetal membranes. The placenta is delivered within half an hour of the pup's birth, though it is occasionally delivered with the pup, in which case the cord fails to break, and the pup trails cord and placenta around with it for a number of days.

At birth the pup is about 18 inches long and has a thick, black woolly coat, the males showing a little grizzling around the mouth and head, owing to the presence of white-tipped guard hairs.

The first maternal reaction after birth is a high pitched howling. The pup answers this call with a bleat, and the two then howl and bleat at each other for a number of minutes, at the end of which they are able to recognise each other's voices. By this means alone the mother is able to identify her pup at a distance, although the final confirmation is by smell.

The pup tries to suckle from any cow, but a mother will only feed her own pup, and drives off all others. The milk of the Fur Seals of South Georgia has a higher concentration of fat and protein than other Fur Seals, 26.4 per cent fat (cf. Cape Fur Seal 18.6 per cent), and 22.4 per cent protein (cf. Cape Fur Seal 10 per cent). This difference may be due to the harsh environment at South Georgia, and the comparatively short lactation period of the seals who inhabit the island.

For the first week or so the pups do not usually wander far from their mothers, but if they do the cows follow, though the bull tries to prevent a cow leaving the confines of his harem. A cow molested by the bull retaliates with a snap at his whiskers; he is never actually bitten, but the snap is sufficient to deter him. Hunters have discovered this Achilles heel, and have found that an attacking male can be calmed by tickling his whiskers with a pole.

While the cows are away at sea for short periods the pups gather in 'pods' at the back of the beaches and spend their time playing and sleeping, the females mock-fighting and growling fiercely at each other. On returning to the rookery the mother at once 'howls' and the appropriate pup answers with its distinctive bleat. When recognition is complete the mother removes her pup to a quiet part of the beach and suckles it.

The breeding beaches become gradually more and more deserted as the females move away either to the water or to feed their young, and by the middle of January the harems have started to break up. By then the harem bulls are emaciated and exhausted, and make their way to the sea. Some of the territories are then taken over by younger males, who start to gather females into their own harems, but it appears that no copulation takes place.

From the end of January to the beginning of March the pups pass through their first moult to a silvery grey; the adult cows follow, and then the adult bulls. During the moult many of the animals stay on land, returning only occasionally to the water for short feeding expeditions.

The main exodus of breeding cows and pups is in April; by then the pups have suckled for between three and three-and-a-half months, and are more or less independent. Some of the young males return intermittently until the end of June, but between June and November the beaches are almost deserted.

The male pups become sexually mature long before they start to breed, and are capable of complete copulation at 3 years of age. At 4 they become aquatic bulls, and sometimes copulate with cows leaving the rookery, but it is not until they are 6 or more that they may become harem bulls. The females are sexually mature at 2 years of age, and bear their first pups at 3 years.

The species in relation to man

The sealing history of the species follows the familiar pattern, with hunting at its height in the early nineteenth century. At this time there were about thirty sealing vessels of American, Russian and British origin hunting seals off South Georgia, and annual hauls were up to 57,000 skins per vessel. By 1822 an average of 1,250,000 skins were being taken every year, and the colonies were practically wiped out, for at that time nearly all the seals that hauled out on the rookeries were killed, and the loss of pups left without mothers must have been something like 100,000.

Fifty years later the colonies were revisited by another generation of sealers, who over the next sixteen years killed 45,000 seals. At the end of this period, in 1888, the species was believed to be literally extinct, but a small colony was discovered on Bird Island in 1933.

A breeding colony on the Prince Edward Islands in the southern Indian Ocean was exploited in 1921, but only about 800 skins were taken before hunting became commercially unprofitable.

The quality of the underfur is midway between that of the Pribilof and Cape Fur Seals, but numbers have been reduced below profitable level.

At present the species is protected on many islands, and licences are necessary in order to hunt seals on all the British islands, on the French islands of Crozet, St Paul, Amsterdam and Kerguelen, and on the Norwegian island of Bouvet.

4. The Sealions

STELLER'S SEALION (Plate 3)   *Eumetopias jubatus*

Distribution and population

Steller's Sealion is a widely distributed and quite numerous species, found throughout the North Pacific and Bering Sea; from Santa Barbara in southern California, to Hokkaido, the northern island of Japan; from Walrus Island in the Pribilofs to Kodiak Island off the south coast of Alaska; from Kamchatka, a peninsula of Siberia at the western limits of the Bering Sea, to Herschel Island well inside the Arctic Circle; and a huge colony is present on the Aleutians where there are estimated to be at least 100,000 individuals — about one third of the world population.

Appearance and description

The adult male is a large and heavy animal, measuring up to 11 feet in length and weighing up to 1 ton, and is considerably larger than the female, who rarely exceeds 8½ feet and tips the scales at about 600 pounds. The colour of the fur in both sexes is variable, but is usually a yellowish shade of buff. The male develops a thick and very muscular neck bearing a substantial mane of long coarse hairs.

A characteristic feature of the species is the unusual appearance of the eyes. Around the outer edges of the iris of each eye there is a circle of white, which gives the animals a frightening, staring and ferocious expression.

Habitat and habits

Squids form the major part of the diet, but this sealion also eats a wide variety of fish including cod, lampreys, halibut, and herring. In line with other species, they also swallow stones.

Many seals have a phenomenally long intestine compared to that of most land carnivores, and the Steller's Sealion seems to have one of the longest. The intestine of one old female 7 feet in length was measured, and it was found that the large intestine was 9 feet 3 inches long, and the small intestine reached the almost incredible measurement of 254 feet 9 inches, making a total of 264 feet — an intestine thirty-eight times the length of the body. There is apparently much variation in individual animals, as other measurements on the same species have been found to be only twenty times the body length. On an average, Steller's Sealion may be said to have a very long gut, and this may prove to be correlated with the diet, although this is by no means certain.

Except during the breeding season, this species is very shy and wary of strangers, human or animal, and is very difficult to approach. Hunters have had great difficulty in getting within rifle-shot range of a herd without being observed. As soon as the intruder has been spotted the animals desert the beaches for the comparative safety of the water. During the breeding season, however, they lose their timidity; the cows stick close to their pups and stand their ground, and the young bulls do the same. The adult bulls are not so courageous, and are inclined to flee. Some cows decide that the safety of their pups must come first, and therefore take their young to the water, leading them to some safer spot. During the breeding season, it is said that if a stone is thrown at a cow, no matter how short the range, or how hard it is thrown, the cow will catch it in her mouth, even if this action results in her breaking some teeth. She bites the stone savagely and then throws it aside. She will take the same attitude if she is poked with a stick or pole. She will wrench it from the hand, chew it, and throw it disdainfully aside. Apart from man, when he is able to get close enough, the species has few natural enemies, although Killer Whales have been known to attack solitary individuals.

Steller's Sealions have the peculiarity that they must be either right in the water or right out of it, and cannot bear to be half in and half out of the water at tide line; they will not allow themselves to be washed by the waves. When they want to leave the water they do not crawl up the beach, but leap straight from the water on to some rock which is high and dry, well out of the water. When returning to the water they dive from some high spot straight into the sea. They appear to be able to judge the depth of the water into which they are diving, and adjust their angle of descent accordingly.

Seasonal movements

Seasonal movements have been recorded, but they seem to be different in the northern and southern parts of the range of the species. For example, very few males have been seen on the Californian coast during the winter, and it is currently believed that they migrate northwards, to return south again in the early summer of the following year. The adult and sub-adult males of the Aleutians, on the other hand, move northwards in the late summer and proceed as far as St Lawrence and Nunivak, and even as far as the Bering Strait in some cases, to return southwards again when the winter ice begins to form.

Reproduction

At the beginning of May the bulls make their way to the rookeries, to be followed two or three weeks later by the cows. Each harem bull establishes his territory and forms a harem of between ten and twenty cows. The pregnant cows give birth to their pups about a week after their arrival at the rookeries, and the greatest number of pups are born during the first week of June. Copulation takes place after the pups have been born, and covers a period from the end of May to the middle of July, although the resulting blastocysts do not implant until the following October.

Birth to maturity

At birth the pup is about 3½ feet long and weighs at least 40 pounds. The new born young is covered with a very thick, dull brown pelt, moulted at about six months, when a dark brown coat takes its place. By the second year most individuals have achieved the lighter adult colour. Albinos have been recorded, and these have pink flippers and eyelids. Like most albinos, they appear to have very poor eyesight.

There are usually more male pups than female, possibly due to a higher infant mortality rate amongst the very young females. The ratio of males to females at six months is about three to one.

The body weight of a pup doubles during the first seven weeks, and the length of the body increases by about 25 per cent. Until about ten weeks of age there is little difference in size between the sexes, but after this the males start to put on weight, and grow much faster than the females.

By the end of July many of the pups, who until then have lived wholly on land, have taken to the water and started to obtain solid food for themselves. The adult cows continue to give milk for at least three months after the birth of the pups, and possibly even until the following year when the next season's pups are born. By the time the pups are a year old they are more or less independent of their parents, and at three years of age the females are sexually mature, the males two years later.

The species in relation to man

Late in the nineteenth century a colony of Steller's Sealions inhabited Seal Rocks, off the Cliff House near the entrance to the Golden Gate at San Francisco. This colony was rightly regarded as one of the 'sights of Frisco', and their close proximity to the mainland made the sealions a great attraction to tourists, especially during the breeding season, when the rocks would be covered with the sealions.

Some years later the local marine fishermen started to shoot at the colony on Seal Rocks, because they claimed that the sealions were getting the 'lion's share' of the marketable fish in the vicinity. The fishermen were acting contrary to a County Ordinance forbidding the killing of these animals, but they persisted in the slaughter. The Ordinance was never enforced by the authorities, and the colony was wiped out. At present the only sealion one is likely to see near Seal Rocks is an occasional lone straggler.

Commercial hunting was undertaken in the late nineteenth century, when the oil, skins, and trimmings were in great demand. But at Santa Barbara only a remnant of the hide trade remained in 1909. In the early twentieth century the salted, half-dried hides were worth about five cents a pound, and were used mainly for the production of cheap low grade leather. This small industry persisted until the killing of the species was outlawed some years later.

Even in the 1930s the trimmings of Steller's Sealions were in great demand by China, and a set of genitalia, whiskers, and gall bladder was valued at about five American dollars. The Chinese used the whiskers as pipe-cleaners, the

E

genitalia as the basis of aphrodisiacs, and the gall bladder was supposed to have a variety of medicinal properties.

The present day fishermen still complain of Steller's Sealion damaging marketable hauls of fish, including salmon, from the nets. Specific charges have been proved, but it has also been shown that the sealions gather near the nets to catch lampreys, which are a great danger to salmon.

Parts of Steller's Sealion are still used by the Aleuts and Eskimos, who make the intestinal membranes into suits of waterproof clothing. The complete suit weighs only a pound and can be carried in the pocket, just like a 'plastic mac'. The pelts are also used to make leather for Mukluks or leggings.

The species in captivity

Sealions of this species are rarely seen in captivity as they have a rather belligerent nature and cannot be readily tamed or trained. One, however, did arrive at the National Zoological Park in Washington in 1900, and survived there for seventeen years.

THE CALIFORNIAN SEALION (Plate 4)   *Zalophus californianus*

Distribution and population

The Californian Sealion is, in this country at least, the species most often seen in Zoological Gardens. It is also usually a troupe of Californian Sealions which is billed by circuses as 'Performing Seals', for they are easily trained, and both zoos and circuses make full use of their talents.

There are three distinct sub-species:

Z.c. californianus, which occurs along the coast of California from the Fallarones to the Gulf of California. It is also found on a number of small islands off the mainland including Santa Barbara, Los Coronados, Guadalupe, Cedros, and Sonoran. The population of this sub-species is believed to be in the region of 50,000.

A second sub-species, *Z.c. wollebaeki*, occurs on the Galapagos Islands, where the population is estimated at about 20,000.

The third sub-species, *Z.c. japonicus*, inhabits both the western and eastern coasts of the southern half of the Honshu Island of Japan. This Japanese colony is precariously close to extinction, recent estimates of the population being as low as 300.

The three sub-species, while differing in distribution, vary little anatomically, although the Galapagos race appears to have a somewhat smaller and narrower skull than the other forms.

Appearance and description

Californian Sealions are medium-sized, sleek, streamlined animals with big, round, soft eyes, and fairly long muzzles. The males attain lengths of 7 feet and weights of 600 pounds; the females 6 feet and 200 pounds. The colour of the fur is variable, but it is always some shade of chocolate brown, the top of the head becoming lighter with age. The adult male has a noticeably raised fore-head, due to the skull bearing an unusually high sagittal crest.

Habitat and habits

Although the Californian Sealion has been kept with great success by zoos and circuses all over the world, and its habits in captivity have been carefully studied and noted, little work has been carried out on the species in the wild. Our knowledge of the animals' natural way of life remains sketchy.

Sealions have few natural enemies, although they are occasionally attacked by Killer Whales and sharks. The food supply of the sealion is normally restricted to squids and octopuses, but they will take hake, herring, and rock fish when the opportunity offers. Given a choice between a cephalopod and a salmon they show a distinct preference for the cephalopod.

They are naturally playful beasts, and chase each other in the water to accompanying honks and barks; they have also been seen to chase their own exhaled air bubbles. The yearlings are the most playful, and can often be seen dolphin-jumping in a long line, sometimes leaping clean over each other's backs.

On land they are continually active, due to the parasitic infestations which irritate the skin, and which are found in all individuals. Other organic complaints have been found frequently in animals captured from the wild state, such as lesions of the aorta, and stomach ulcers. All these troubles can be treated and cured when the animals are kept in captivity, where clean fish, regular meals, sanitation, and medical care can be provided. Californian Sealions have often been found with their pelts badly marked with cuts and sores, but these injuries may have been inflicted by the sharp stones of the black lava that is found in many of their habitats. These injuries, too, can be successfully treated, and prevented while the animals are in captivity.

Captain Henry Pain of the S.S. *Scanderia* suggested that the stones in the stomachs of the Californian Sealions were for ballast, for keeping the animal down in the water so that it could catch fish more easily. He states that more stones are found in animals just hauled out, which are very fat, than in those which have not fed for some time and are very thin.

The animals often enter and leave the water in large groups of thirty to forty.

Seasonal movements

Although sealions are present off the coasts of California all the year round, there is evidence of some seasonal movement. Many of the bulls are believed to move northwards during the winter, as they have been reported off the Oregon and Washington coasts at that time of year, and some have been sighted as far north as Vancouver Island. The reverse movement occurs with the coming of spring. Whether or not similar movements occur amongst the Galapagos and Japanese colonies has not been established.

Reproduction

The greatest gap in our knowledge of the species concerns its reproduction. Sealions breed on sandy, rocky, or boulder-strewn beaches, and in a great many places the rookeries are backed by high precipitous cliffs, making the breeding places almost inaccessible from the landward side. Individuals have also been found in long, maze-like caves which have been worn into the cliffs of rocky islands; pups have been found in such places, but it is not known whether they were bred there, or deposited by their parents for safety.

The few observations that have been made during the breeding season suggest that the harems are very loosely organised, with the bulls patrolling their territories and copulating with the cows shortly after the birth of the pups.

Except for the Galapagos colony, the pups are born at the end of May and in early June. In the Galapagos, which are on the Equator and partly to the south of it, the pups are born between October and December. At birth the pups are up to $2\frac{1}{2}$ feet in length, weigh between 12 and 14 pounds, and are covered with a rich, chestnut-brown coat. In captivity the female has been seen to eat the placenta shortly after it is expelled. Many other animals do this and the habit is probably general among sealions in the wild state, but it has still to be verified by observations in the field. The majority of the pups born in captivity have taken to the water after about ten days, although one in New York Zoo did not take the plunge until its second month. Behaviour in the wild has not been studied. The pups suckle for about six months, and are gradually weaned on to a solid diet. The milk of the cow contains no lactose, and consists of 36 per cent fat, and 14 per cent protein (the chief protein being casein).

Observations made on the Galapagos colony (*Z.c. wollebaeki*) by Eibl Eibesfeldt are of the greatest interest, but do not necessarily apply to all the sub-species. He noticed that the harem bulls patrolled the waters off their beach territories. When neighbouring bulls met they did not fight unless one intruded upon the territory of the other, but they did raise themselves up in a stiff and formal manner, roaring at each other in warning. Eibesfeldt found that the bulls were aggressive towards him if he remained crouching below or at the same level as the sealion when raised in threat. But if he drew himself up to his full height, much taller than the sealion, the animal appeared frightened. The ability to raise itself up higher than its opponent's eye-level may thus be an important factor for a sealion in winnings its battles.

On land the bulls paid very little attention to the pups, but when the pups entered the water the bulls showed a strong protective instinct. If a pup started to swim out into deep water, a bull headed it off and chased it back landwards. In the evening the cows entered the water to feed, and each was greeted by the appropriate bull, who stayed in the water until the last cow and pup were safely back on land. Only then did he come out of the water and rest for the night. Eibesfeldt did not observe any of the bulls eating whilst they were on land, but he concluded that they had done some fishing while they were patrolling the offshore waters during the day. When not suckling, the pups were seen to play with pebbles and driftwood, and to mock-fight and snap at each other without actually biting.

In some of the localities where sealions were observed, notably on Cedros

Island, frightened pups would rush for their fathers, and start nuzzling up to them. The bulls returned the nuzzling, and appeared concerned for the welfare of the youngsters. This contrasts with the bull's attitude in captivity where it has been reported that if a pup fell into the water before it could swim properly, the male showed concern but left the rescue to the cow.

The species in relation to man

Captain Scammon headed a sealing expedition to Santa Barbara in 1852, and of his hunting he wrote that 'None but adult males were captured, which was usually by shooting them in the ear or near it; for a ball in any other part of the body had no more effect than it would in a Grizzly Bear. Occasionally, however, they are taken with the club and lance. . . .'. Scammon then went on to describe how the hunters pulled out the longest of the seals' whiskers, skinned the animals, and cut up the blubber from the carcasses into sections before taking it out to the waiting ship to be minced and boiled for oil extraction. The 'trimmings' were also apparently important, as they were in great demand from China, where they were used as aphrodisiacs and for medicinal purposes.

In the early nineteenth century large numbers of sealions were killed on the Californian coasts, providing thousands of barrels of oil. At least three sealions had to be killed to obtain one barrel of oil.

At that time there was no market for the skins, but some years later they became profitable for making glue-stock.

The species in captivity

The popularity of Californian Sealions in zoos and circuses is due to their ability to learn tricks, and although it may take some time to teach a trick it is seldom forgotten once learnt. Their performing life is about ten years, which is another sound reason for their popularity with circuses where money may be lost while new animals are trained.

Records of the species living in captivity for twelve to fourteen years are common, and two specimens at the London Zoo are at least 18 years of age.

Causes of death in captivity have in many cases been traced to tuberculosis, peritonitis, and roundworm infections of the heart and main blood vessels. The tuberculosis has presumably been contracted from man.

THE SOUTHERN SEALION (Plate 3)   *Otaria byronia*

Distribution and population

The Southern Sealion has been known since the sixteenth century when the
early voyagers fully appreciated this welcome source of meat, oil, and fur after
sailing for many, months on a diet of salt meat and ship's biscuit. But the
Southern Sealion does not appear to have undergone the intensive hunting
suffered by other species during the eighteenth and nineteenth centuries. At
present the population is the largest of all the sealion species, being estimated
at not less than 800,000, and it may exceed a million. This abundance may well
be due to the comparative inactivity of the sealers.

The Southern Sealion is found on both the Pacific and Atlantic coasts of
South America, from southern Brazil around the Cape to Peru, and there are
also colonies on the Falkland Islands. On the South American mainland there
are estimated to be 400,000 individuals, 200,000 of which inhabit some sixty or
so rookeries along the Argentinian coast. A further 400,000 are believed to
inhabit the Falkland Islands.

Appearance and description

A distinctive characteristic of the species is the great variation in colour
between individuals. The majority of the males are dark brown with a lighter
mane, dark yellow belly, and reddish-brown furred flippers, but individual
males have been recorded as grey, and others as gold. The same variation is
displayed by the females. Most of the cows are dark brown on the back, with
the head and nape a dull yellow, and the belly a dark yellow, but the whole of
the head and neck may be yellow, and specimens have been recorded which
had yellow backs, and still others with cream upper parts. This lack of uni-
formity was doubtless responsible for the many arguments amongst early
naturalists over the numbers of species or sub-species.

In size and weight the males, as with other sealions, outstrip the females, the
bulls attaining lengths of 8 feet, against 6 feet for cows, and weights of 1,200

pounds against 300 pounds. Occasionally much larger bulls have been recorded, the largest weighing over 1,500 pounds.

The bull has a characteristic moustache of straw-coloured bristles which may reach a length of 12 inches on each side of the muzzle. The bristles are moved by surface muscles, and when the mouth is opened they are rotated downwards and forwards forming a type of screen on each side of the jaws.

Habitat and habits

When excited the Southern Sealion is capable of travelling over a rough beach with great speed, and can easily keep pace with a running man. Although movement over land is difficult for them, and they are soon out of breath and forced to rest, sealions of this species have been found at considerable distances from the sea. There have been reports of emaciated specimens being found many miles inland, and these sightings of weak, thin animals have given rise to local beliefs that they travel inland to die. This is at least doubtful, and the fact that they look so near to death is probably due to a starvation diet during their journey from the shore. The reason for the occasional movement of one or two sealions away from the coast is unknown, and it is certainly not a normal occurrence.

Southern Sealions are expert swimmers and divers; they will launch themselves into the water from considerable heights, and demonstrate their great strength and skill by swimming ashore in very heavy surf. When speed is required in the water the hindquarters and flippers are used as sculls, and while streaking through the water they often leap out with each breath, in much the same way, although not as gracefully, as the Fur Seals. They will spend hours playing together in the water and carry out the most complicated manoeuvres with consummate ease, a favourite variation being swimming on their backs. Very rough surf does not deter them from play, but they appear to understand when it is too dangerous to attempt a landing.

On land they are gregarious, and on leaving the water an individual heads straight for a group of his fellows. The cows, immature bulls and pups lie in any position, sometimes on top of one another, but the adult bulls, who are friendly towards each other except during the breeding season, lie alongside and use each other as pillows. They are very vocal beasts, the males emitting deep, powerful husky roars and coughs, mingled with grunts and groans and loud belches.

The cows are a little less noisy, but they too have strong voices and sound like domestic calves.

The attitude of these sealions to man is inconsistent. Some of the disturbed animals appear to be simply uneasy, others cough in anger and charge, and during the breeding season cowless bulls have been known to chase men for long distances. Although they sometimes appear to be wary of intruders, they are extremely inquisitive animals, and usually investigate any strange object on their beach. They seem frightened only of objects taller than their own eye-level, a characteristic shared by the Galapagos race of the Californian Sealion.

The sealion's sight is thought to play quite a large part in its underwater hunting, but on land vision seems poor, the animals letting their eyelids droop, perhaps to reduce the amount of light on the sensitive retina. On the shore their sense of smell is useful, and they will detect the scent of a man at 200 yards.

Their feeding ground is mainly in coastal shallow waters, but occasionally they wander far out to sea to hunt. The food is similar to that of other species, consisting of squids, crustaceans (mainly *Munida*), small fish, and penguins. The squids and Munida are plentiful around the coasts of both Argentina and the Falkland Islands. The stomach of the Southern Sealion is very muscular and has been found to contain up to 20 pounds of stones, which may be either round and smooth, or sharp and jagged. The discovery of rough stones has led to suggestions that they have a function similar to that of the grit in the gizzard of a bird, or that the stones destroy parasitic nematodes in the stomach of the sealion. A further theory, partly verified, is concerned with the pups. A young pup when swimming is somewhat top heavy and, if the pup did not ingest stones to weigh down the rear half of its body, it would be swimming with its head down under water. The whole question is, however, complicated by the fact that Sealions from the Falkland Islands are not known to ingest stones at all.

Seasonal movements

There is no evidence to suggest that any seasonal movements occur; the only movements are to and from the feeding grounds.

Reproduction

The breeding season, which lasts from August to February, has been closely studied in the wild; and, in contrast to our ignorance of many other species, the observations are both full and accurate. During the time that the bulls are claiming and defending their territories, the rookery is a veritable battlefield, with the bulls roaring and fighting and blood flowing freely. They are still extremely irritable when the cows arrive. The cows, although returning to the same beach year after year to breed, often haul out on an adjoining beach before finally arriving at the rookery. On arrival they advance hesitatingly up the beach until noticed by a bull. The bull conveys interest and pleasure, and the cow then settles in his harem, which may contain up to a dozen other cows. Each harem bull knows the limits of his territory and patrols its boundary. Once a cow is a member of a harem she is not allowed to leave it; the bull will even go so far as to lift her bodily and carry her back to her correct position should she begin to wander out of his territory. Fights between bulls break out frequently, and each tries with his teeth to obtain a grip on the neck of the other. Once a good hold has been obtained there is much pushing and shaking. The vanquished bull is finally released and chased away, the conqueror snapping and slashing at the flanks and rear of his retreating adversary. Many fights reach no decision, both assailants fighting to a standstill. They are quick, clever, and agile combatants, and avoid many vicious bites, but even when severely wounded the bulls appear to be insensitive to the pain; their rage merely increases. So much fighting leaves the older bulls with many scars, but the immature animals are peaceable and their pelts remain unmarked. It is therefore these youngsters which are the targets of the fur-hunters. The adult cows fight amongst themselves, but usually the harem bulls are able to keep them under control.

Copulation begins soon after the birth of the pups, but it is preceded by elaborate courtship. The bull and the cow face each other, moving their heads from side to side, and in doing so caress each other on the sides and front of the neck, occasionally 'kissing' by rubbing their mouths together. Sometimes the cow lightly grips the neck of the bull with her teeth. After this phase they both move backwards a little and stick their snouts in the air. Copulation seldom follows directly on this courtship. The cow sometimes attempts to excite the bull by presenting her hindquarters to him; she then bends over backwards and grips the bull's neck, and tries to pull him towards her, but this is seldom effective. Often when the bull does try to copulate, the cow moves away, and the frustrated male snaps and growls. The bull is eventually successful and after copulation the cow is allowed to return to the water, coming on land at intervals to feed the pup. When all the cows have been served, the harems start to disintegrate, and the bulls, who have been on land without food or much sleep for about two months, make their way to some quiet spot and sleep. During the next six months, from February onwards, they feed and recover their strength, and their thin emaciated bodies take on the rotund and healthy appearance of the pre-breeding season animals.

Birth to maturity

The pups are born at night or early in the morning, between late December and mid January, most of them during the first week of the new year. The placentae and membranes which litter the rookery are cleared away by the scavenging skuas and gulls. (Unlike the Californian Sealions the mothers do not appear to eat the afterbirths.)

At birth the pup is about $2\frac{1}{2}$ feet long and is covered with thick black fur, which fades to a dark chocolate colour, and continues to fade as the pup grows older until it is dark and grizzled at the end of the first year. The first moult then takes place, the new rust-brown fur appearing first on the face, then on the neck, followed by the flanks, rump, and back. The period of moulting is spread over the months April to August, and the pups do not all moult at the same time.

The cows return to the water after the birth of their young but land to suckle the pups at regular intervals. While the cows are away the pups gather in groups or 'pods', and spend the time sleeping or playing with their contemporaries in or near the water. They will not go out into deep water unless they are coaxed to do so by their mothers, and even then try to seek refuge on the backs of the cows. At about 6 months most of the pups are weaned and at $3\frac{1}{2}$ years of age the females are sexually mature, the males a year or so later.

The species in relation to man

Drake reported that his sailors had 'kylled some seyles for our provysyon', and later took 'two hundred in the space of one hour'. The seals were an important source of fresh food for the early voyagers along the Patagonian coast. The livers of the 'seyles' were reported by Drake's men to be poisonous, causing 'fevers and headaches to everyone who eat them, and presently all the hair on their bodies falls off and some die'; but Hamilton in *Discovery Reports* of 1934 and 1939 states that he ate some without effect. Hamilton's courageous experiment suggests that the damage to Drake's sailors was caused not by the livers being poisonous but rather to the fact that the sailors were overcome by the surfeit of rich food.

In the 1930s an attempt to exploit the Falkland Island sealion was uneconomical, although about 14 gallons of oil were harvested for each bull killed.

At present, the killing of sealions is allowed under licence in South America and the Falklands, but only Argentina has formed a small industry and is exploiting the species commercially.

The species in captivity

The London Zoo kept a Southern Sealion for over seventeen years, but it is thought that the species lives to twenty or more years of age in the wild.

THE AUSTRALIAN SEALION (Plate 5)   *Neophoca cinerea*

Distribution and population

Detailed accounts of the habits of the Australian Sealion, as of the Australian species of fur seal, are almost non-existent. Although the species is not plentiful, there are sufficient numbers for study; they remain, nevertheless, one of the least familiar of the Pinnipedia. Their general habits are known, but few detailed observations have been recorded.

There are colonies on the coastlines, islands and rocks in the Great Australian Bight, from Kangaroo Island (off Adelaide) to the Houtman Rocks (off the coast of Western Australia).

Recent estimates of the population of the species vary a great deal, ranging from 2,000 to 10,000 individuals. It is, however, generally agreed that they are 'not very abundant.'

Appearance and description

The males are very large animals, and reach 12 feet in length. The coat of the adult bull is dark brown with a yellowish mane of coarser hairs. The younger bulls, before the development of the mane, have a lighter brown patch around the neck. The cows are generally smaller than the bulls, although they may attain 10 feet in length. The fur is a rich brown on the back, lightening along the flanks to yellowish underneath the body.

Habitat and habits

The Australian Sealion is noted for its ability to climb cliffs and travel inland; individuals have been known to move as much as 6 miles from the sea.

They are agile hunters and the two staple ingredients of their diet are penguins and fish. In common with many other species of Pinnipede, stones have been discovered in the stomach.

Seasonal movements

The species is non-migratory, and individuals rarely move far from their place of birth. If an animal does venture out to sea on a short trip, it returns unerringly to the same beach from which it set out.

Reproduction

The breeding season lasts from October to early December, and bulls collect an average of about five cows. Unlike the bulls of most other species, the male Australian Sealion does not fast, but makes regular hunting trips for food throughout the breeding season. At the end of the season, therefore, the bulls are fit and healthy, in striking contrast to the emaciated appearance of males of other species at the end of their rutting seasons.

Birth to maturity

The pups are born early in December, covered with thick brown fur and a dense underfur which is lost in the first few months of life, leaving the longer, but less dense, adult coat. It is not known how long the pup is dependent on the mother, but it is probably weaned after six or seven months, following gradual lengthening of the periods between each feed.

HOOKER'S SEALION (Plate 5)   *Phocarctos hookeri*

Distribution and population

Of the two species of sealion associated with Australasia Hooker's is the better known, because it is present in greater numbers than the Australian Sealion, and in comparatively restricted localities. Whereas Australian Sealions are spread throughout the Great Australian Bight, Hooker's Sealions are found mainly on Auckland and Campbell Islands. They are occasionally seen on Macquarie, and very rarely on the very southern tip of the South Island of New Zealand.

The population is believed to be between 10,000 and 50,000; although this is considerably greater than that of the Australian species, the Auckland and Campbell sealions are by no means out of danger of extinction. Auckland is now a Nature Reserve, affording the protection necessary to increase, or at least maintain, numbers.

Appearance and description

The mature bulls are dark brown, with a thick, well developed mane of longer and darker hairs. The bulls grow up to 10 feet, some 3 or 4 feet longer than the cows. The sexes may be distinguished by colour as well as by size difference; the coat of the female being much lighter in colour than that of the male, and the mane absent.

Habitat and habits

Hooker's Sealions favour flat, sandy, rock-free beaches, and like their Australian relatives have an inclination to wander inland in rough grass country.

Food is plentiful: small fish, molluscs and crustaceans are abundant around the rocky coasts of the islands and in the shallow rock pools. As well as catching fish and shelled creatures, the sealions have been seen to chase and catch penguins, which they take out to deeper water and tear apart. The sealion eats the flesh and discards the skin and bones. The Red Crab, one of the sealions' favourite titbits, is eaten in the same way, but in this case it seems that the sealion lands to digest the meal, and regurgitates the undigested remains of the crab.

Seasonal movements

The species appears to make no seasonal movements, presumably because there is a plentiful food supply at hand all the year round, and there is no great variation in climate between the seasons.

Reproduction

The breeding season starts in early October, the spring of the southern hemisphere. The cows, which arrive at the rookeries early in November, a month or so after the bulls, find the beaches already well organised into sections, each harem bull claiming and defending his own territory. A bull maintains about a dozen cows, and mating begins soon after the birth of the pups. The breeding season continues until the end of January, by which time most of the cows have been served, and the majority of the pups are old enough to venture into the water. As the harems begin to disintegrate, the bulls end their long fast and head for the water and food.

Birth to maturity

The majority of pups are born early in the new year, and are covered with rich brown fur. The cows coax their offspring into the water at the age of about a month. Once the pup has taken to the water it spends a great deal of time playing with others in the shallows and rock pools near the beaches where they were born. At fairly regular intervals they are called away from their play to be suckled by their mothers; the length of time between each feed increases over the months, and gradually the youngster starts to supplement its diet with more solid food in the form of fish and crustaceans. By the time the pups are seven months old most of them are weaned, but they remain with their mothers until the following year.

The species in relation to man

One of the earliest accounts of the species was given by Sir James Ross, during the voyages of the ships *Erebus* and *Terror* between 1835 and 1843. He states that his men killed a number of sealions on Auckland for the meat, oil and leather.

The numbers are not at present large enough to attract commercial hunters, and Auckland Island is also a Nature Reserve.

Seals of the World

Male Northern Fur Seal
Guadalupe Fur Seal
Southern Fur Seal, Galapagos
race

b

c

2. Seals of the World

a. South African Fur Seal and pup
b. Australian Fur Seal and pup
c. Kerguelen Fur Seal, male and harem
d. New Zealand Fur Seal
e. Kerguelen Fur Seal pups

a

b

c

d

e

Seals of the World

Southern Sealion
Southern Sealions
Male Steller's Sealion
Male Steller's Sealions fighting

c

d

4. Seals of the World

a. Californian Sealions
b. Californian Sealion
c. Californian Sealions, male and
   female

a

b

c

6. Seals of the World

a. Young Pacific Walrus

7. Seals of the World

a. Southern Elephant Seal pups
b. Male Southern Elephant Seal
c. Male Southern Elephant Seal,
   proboscis inflated

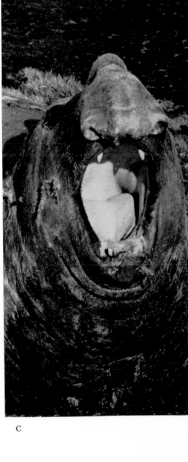

c

b

8 & 9. Seals of the World

a. Hooded Seal, immature 'blue-
   back'
b. and c. Male Northern Elephant
   Seal
d. Northern Elephant Seals
e. Ross Seal
f. Weddell Seal
g. Leopard Seal, close-up

a

b

c

d

f

g

a

a

c

a

b

12-13. Seals of the World

a. Grey Seals ashore
b. Grey Seals awash
c. Grey Seals mating
d. Grey Seal, new born pup
e. Grey Seal, well fed pup
f. Grey Seal pup moulting

c

d

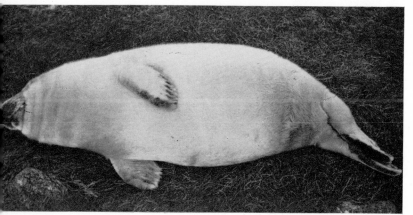

e

f

a

b

c

e

Hawaiian Monk Seal

5. The Walrus
Odobenus rosmarus

(Plate 6)

Distribution and population

Two sub-species of Walrus are acknowledged in the world today — *Odobenus rosmarus rosmarus*, the Atlantic Walrus; and *Odobenus rosmarus divergens*, the Pacific Walrus. The terms 'Atlantic' and 'Pacific' are rather misleading, as both forms are now confined to regions within the Arctic Circle. More specifically, the Pacific Walrus is found along the coasts of north-eastern Siberia and north-western Alaska; and the Atlantic Walrus around the north-western and northern coasts of Greenland and Ellesmere Island, and to a small extent on Bear Island, Spitzbergen, and Novaya Zemlya north of Norway. Estimates of the combined world population vary between 45,000 and 90,000.

One of the earliest accounts of the species was given by Ohthere, a Norwegian sailor, who reported to King Alfred the Great in about the year 890, that he had 'made a voyage beyond Norway for the more commodite of fishing Horse-whales which have in their teeth bones of great price and excellence.' Ohthere brought some of these Horsewhale teeth (Walrus tusks) to show the king. Thus as long ago as the ninth century the value of the ivory tusks of the Walrus was appreciated, but it was not for many centuries that the animals were hunted on a commercial basis.

At one time Walruses were to be found as far south as Nova Scotia in western Canada, but by the end of the eighteenth century, when thousands were killed by hunters for their tusks, pelts and oil, they were all but exterminated from this region, and since that time only an occasional straggler has been seen as far south as Labrador.

On the other side of the Atlantic, Walruses were occasional around Scotland and the Hebrides, though never in concentration. By the early 1900s, following three centuries of persecution, they had become extremely rare.

Fossil remains of the Walrus or its ancestors have been discovered in England

F

and Belgium in Europe, and New Jersey, Virginia, and South Carolina in the United States, indicating that their range included these comparatively southern areas in prehistoric times.

On the Pacific side of North America Walruses were formerly plentiful on the Pribilof Islands, St Matthew Island, and the Alaska coast, but they are now rare outside the Arctic Circle.

Appearance and description

Besides their distribution, the sub-species differ in some anatomical details. The Pacific form has, on the average, longer tusks than its Atlantic counterpart; and, as its scientific name suggests, the tusks tend to diverge and be bowed in the middle. A further distinguishing feature is that the nostrils of the Pacific form are not visible from the front, being situated more on top of the muzzle than in the Atlantic form. In size both sub-species are second only to the huge Elephant Seal, the Walrus bulls attaining lengths of up to 12 feet, and weights of a ton or more. Blubber accounts for almost a third of the total weight. The cows are generally about one third smaller than the bulls. The body of the Walrus is thick and swollen, and the head and muzzle much more rounded than that of the Seal, Fur Seal or Sealion. The characteristic features of the Walrus are, however, the huge tusks, the moustache of bristles, and the sparsely haired body. The external ears are no more than low wrinkles of skin, and no pinnae (ear flaps) are present.

As in all the pinnipeds, the fore and hind limbs have become modified into flippers during the course of evolution, and in the Walrus they are thick and cartilaginous, more particularly at the leading edges. The palms of the fore flippers and soles of the hind are bare, rough and warty, and the hind flippers can be rotated forwards in much the same way as Sealions move theirs. This adaptation enables the Walrus to move over land with remarkable speed; careless hunters, chased by a Walrus, have found that their quarry can run as fast as a man.

The hide may be as much as 2 inches thick, and the blubber beneath a further 6 inches. The moustache consists of some 400 stiff bristles, each of which is richly supplied with blood vessels and nerves. The bristles are sensory in function, and are also used, rather surprisingly, for shovelling food into the mouth.

The tusks, which are the canine teeth, may grow in bulls to a length of 3 feet 6 inches, and weigh up to 12 pounds each; the tusks of the female reach 2 feet in length.

Habitat and habits

During the day, when the herd is out of the water, a sentinel is posted, and at the approach of possible danger, such as a hunter, he gives the alarm call — a low whistling bellow — and the whole herd pours into the sea. If one of the herd is attacked, the rest will defend the victim vigorously, and a slow or clumsy hunter may be badly wounded by tusk slashes.

Walruses are not normally aggressive creatures, but they do on occasions hook their tusks over the side of a boat and capsize it, and have been known to smash their tusks through the bottom planking.

They have few enemies in their bleak and lifeless habitat; none, in fact, but Killer Whales, Polar Bears — and, of course, man, who during the last 300 years has been the greatest danger to the species.

Walruses spend most of their time near the coast, and while feeding sink to the bottom of the water. They feed on bivalve molluscs such as clams and mussels, which they rake up with their tusks. The bristles of the moustache then filter off the debris and push the shellfish into the mouth. There the shells are crushed by the big, flat, pre-molar teeth; the soft parts are swallowed, and the shell fragments rejected through the mouth. The jaws are manipulated by very powerful muscles, and bear in the adult upper jaw: two incisors, two canines (the tusks), and six pre-molars; and in the lower jaw: no incisors, two canines and six pre-molars. Walruses have no molar teeth.

A great deal has been discovered about the diet by examination of stomach contents. Besides molluscs and crustaceans, large quantities of seaweed have been found, but this is probably swallowed unintentionally. Stones have been found in the stomach, but their presence has not been satisfactorily explained. It does not seem likely that they were swallowed accidentally, as the shells of the molluscs are so carefully rejected. It is possible that the stones help to crush up the food in the stomach. A peculiarity of the stomach is that it holds no more than a gallon of food, a strikingly small capacity for such a large animal, and one which will on occasion eat Narwhal, Beluga, or Seal.

Walruses live in herds of mixed sexes and up to a hundred individuals. They are exceedingly vocal — a mixture of loud bellows and elephant-like trumpeting. When hauling out they use their tusks to get a grip on the ice or stone until they can lever themselves over the edge with their fore flippers. The generic name *Odobenus* means 'He who walks (*baino*) with his teeth (*odos*)'. They spend a lot of time on land and can travel quite remarkable distances; over snow they have been known to cover 20 miles.

Ice floes provide Walruses with excellent lazing-grounds, and a whole herd may pile on to a floe in such numbers that the late-comers have to climb on to the backs of others. By that time the floe may become overloaded and tip up, and the whole herd may find itself back in the water. Sunbathing is a popular pastime, and they will lie on the ice for hours, scratching continually with their flippers, for parasites are numerous in the folds of their skin.

Despite their seeming preference for the land, they are highly adapted to life in water, and can swim at speeds of up to 15 miles per hour. They often sleep in the water, in an upright position with their heads above the surface and their bodies submerged. The neck contains a pair of pouches opening into the pharynx, the portion of the alimentary canal at the back of the mouth. By breathing out with the mouth and nostrils closed the pouches can be inflated; muscles around the openings of the pouches then seal them off and keep them inflated as long as required. Each pouch may hold up to a cubic foot of air, and it is possible that they are used as floats. Other suggestions have been put forward: that they provide a reserve air supply when the animal is under water, or that they may be resonating organs for use in conjunction with the vocal cords. The 'Mae West' theory appears to be the most probable, for when a bull is shot in the water the pouches deflate and the animal sinks. A cow, on the other hand, being much lighter, tends to stay afloat when shot. Also, the pouches are generally better developed in the males. There is no evidence to support the other theories, but they cannot be discarded until a great deal more research has gone into the study of the functions of the pharyngeal pouches.

As with other species in the animal kingdom, Elephants for example, 'rogue' or 'outlaw' Walruses occur. These are very large, and their tusks are inclined to be small and sharp, projecting sideways rather than downwards and to the front. These outcasts are avoided by other Walruses, and instead of moving southwards with the herds in the winter they stay in the Arctic. Their feeding habits also differ from the type, in that they will habitually eat seals and other vertebrates that they can catch in Arctic waters.

Seasonal movements

Walruses are migratory, and the general tendency of movement for both the Atlantic and Pacific forms is southwards in the winter, and northwards in the summer. At the approach of winter Pacific Walruses start to move northwards up the coast of Alaska, but do not go further east than Point Barrow. They then head west and pass down the coast of Siberia in a southerly direction. Their method of migration is amazing, for they undertake the journey travelling on floating ice floes. As the ice edge retreats during the summer the herds move northwards with it. Little is known of the migratory habits of the Atlantic sub-species, but the seasonal movements appear to correspond to those of the Pacific form, south in the winter, and north in the summer. During the migrations, herds often haul out on small coastal beaches, and great masses of pink Walruses have been observed in some secluded spots. The older animals are almost devoid of hair, and the pink colour is due to a rise in body temperature on leaving the water, causing the blood vessels to dilate so as to prevent over-heating.

Reproduction

The cows are served during the migration northwards. The minimum breeding age for bulls is between 5 and 6, and for the cows between 4 and 5 years. Copulation probably takes place on land or on ice floes where the herds haul out during their journeys, and although no one has observed copulation, it is believed to occur during the May to June period. This is accepted as the probable time, because most foetuses found in the bodies of cows killed during these months were quite small, a more mature embryo being exceptional. Delayed implantation, if it occurs at all, is very short, and is certainly not as long as in many of the Seals, Fur Seals and Sealions. The period of gestation is between eleven months and a year, when a single calf is born.

Birth to maturity

The milk teeth are lost before birth or soon after, and during the first year or so the enamel cap of the tusk is worn away to expose dentine surrounded by a thin layer of cement. The pulp cavities of the canines remain open, and the tusks therefore continue to grow throughout life. About four-fifths of each tusk is normally exposed; the remainder is embedded in the jaw.

The cow's milk is very rich, containing 35 per cent fat and 12 per cent protein. There are four mammary glands, situated low down on the underside of the cow. Before the calf is weaned it travels with its mother, clinging to her neck by its front flippers, and stays in this position even when the cow is swimming or diving. Weight at birth is between 100 and 150 pounds, length 4 feet, and the calf can swim immediately, though it is some months before it will venture into the water alone. The newly-born calf is covered with grey hair, which changes to brown after the post-natal moult.

The youngster stays with the mother for about two years. The reason for this extended period of weaning appears to be delay in development of the head, which must accommodate the pre-molars, the crushing teeth, before the animal can feed on the adult diet of clams and mussels.

The expectation of life is better now than in the peak years of Walrus hunting. Individuals have attained the age of 30 or more years.

The species in relation to man

During the eighteenth and nineteenth centuries a great industry flourished for the purpose of hunting Ohthere's 'Horsewhales'; this, in conformity with the general pattern, continued until the pursuit of Walruses became commercially unprofitable due to their rapidly approaching extermination.

Eskimos have probably hunted the Walrus since the earliest times, but never commercially. They hunted from domestic need, using the skins to make ropes, and to cover their homes and boats; the ivory for making tools, for carving, and to use in bartering; the flesh as food; and the oil and blubber for fuel. The Eskimos hunted the Walrus with harpoon, line and lance. Having paddled his canoe to an ice floe, the hunter would haul his craft on to the floe, and secure his harpoon line to it through a hole bored in the ice. He would then harpoon any luckless Walrus that happened to be basking nearby. The skin of the Walrus is very thick and tough, and it was not easy to ensure that the harpoon lodged securely in the body. If it did so, the Walrus dived and thrashed in its efforts to dislodge the harpoon. At last, when his quarry was almost exhausted with its efforts, the Eskimo pulled his catch alongside and killed it with a number of stabs from his lance. With the advent of firearms the Eskimo changed his methods but he was probably less successful, as often Walruses shot in the water sank well out of reach. It has been estimated that about 50 per cent of Walruses shot in the water have been lost in this way.

The professional, commercially-motivated Walrus hunters of the eighteenth century employed methods similar to those of the Eskimo, using harpoons and lances, but these hunters worked from boats. They also killed Walruses on land, usually at night, using dogs to break up the herd into smaller groups. The dogs and the darkness caused great confusion in the herd, and the hunters entered the scene with sharp spears.

Whichever method was adopted by the hunters of the eighteenth and nineteenth centuries, they were very successful, and for several years before 1870 the destruction was so great that the annual haul of ivory was in the region of 100,000 pounds weight, accounting for a minimum of 6,000 Walruses. For some years after this date the numbers killed in the Bering Sea area never fell far short of 10,000 to 12,000 annually. By 1890 the yearly taking of ivory had dropped to 12,000 pounds, and the industry found that it was costing more to finance a hunting trip than the expectation in produce.

Whalers, as distinct from purely Walrus hunters, started to pay attention to the Walrus at about the middle of the nineteenth century. Although they probably envisaged Walrus hunting as a side-line, during the years 1868 to 1873 the whalers took at least 60,000 Walruses per year, yielding 50,000 barrels of oil. After 1873 the Walrus population was so depleted that the whalers returned to their primary occupation.

Walruses are still hunted today, but not to the extent of the early years. The Eskimos of Siberia kill between 4,000 and 6,000 annually, and this does not appear to have any drastic effect on the Walrus population. The Eskimos of Alaska and of Greenland, too, still hunt Walruses, but although the Walrus supplies some of the domestic needs of the people, they also export the raw materials to other parts of the world.

Walruses are polygamous, and as long as the hunters confine themselves to the bulls, the remaining males will serve the females and the total population will remain constant.

The species in captivity

Walruses have been kept in Zoological Gardens on both sides of the Atlantic, but the early attempts to keep them in captivity were not successful, the animals dying within the first month. Some of the difficulties have been ironed out over the years, and the greatest success to date has been that of the Zoological Gardens in Copenhagen, where an Atlantic Walrus named 'Thora' was kept in the Gardens from 1937 until she died in 1949, thus surviving in captivity for almost twelve years.

The difficulty in rearing a young Walrus lies in providing a suitable substitute for the mother's milk, which is very rich. Even if the substitute is adequate the youngster may have become accustomed to some other food, such as fish, during its transport to the Zoo.

New York Zoological Society has been successful with a formula consisting of twelve parts undiluted evaporated milk, seven parts corn oil, and one part cod-liver oil. As the Walrus becomes older the diet can be changed by adding increasing amounts of solid food, such as shelled clams and herring, until weaning is complete.

A healthy adult Walrus has an enormous appetite. The greatest recorded weight for a Walrus in captivity is that given for 'Olaf', a male at the New York Aquarium, who was weighed while in transit to a new pool. In 1962, at an estimated 7 years of age, and perhaps still not full grown, 'Olaf' weighed 1,880 pounds and was eating 140 pounds of fish every day.

Now that successful methods of housing and feeding Walruses in captivity have been established, we may hope for a period of research into their unknown anatomy and physiology; we should soon have definite evidence about the true role of the pharyngeal pouches, and the ingested stones, and many outstanding problems may be solved should Walruses be induced to breed in captivity.

6. The Proboscis Seals

The Seal Family, the Phocidae, is usually divided into four sub-families, the Phocinae (which includes most of the northern hemisphere seals), the Lobodontinae (Antarctic Seals), the Monachinae (Monk Seals), and the Cystophorinae, a sub-family comprised of only three species, the two species of Elephant Seal, and the Bladdernose Seal. In many ways these three are the most remarkable of all the seals.

The scientific name, Cystophorinae, means 'those which carry a bladder' and refers to their proboscis. All three have a highly specialised snout, modified into an inflatable proboscis, the form of which differs in the three species. The teeth also differ slightly from those of other seals.

The Cystophorinae include the largest of all the pinnipedes, the Southern Elephant Seal, which is generally bigger and heavier than the huge Walrus of the Arctic seas. The heaviest Elephant Seal may weigh up to 4 tons, but although the Bladdernose Seal is much smaller its nose is equally extraordinary.

The majority of the world's seals are monogamous, and the Bladdernose Seal conforms to this pattern, but Elephant Seals form harems and are as gregarious in the breeding season as the fur seals and sealions.

THE SOUTHERN ELEPHANT SEAL (Plate 7)   *Mirounga leonina*

Distribution and population

The circumpolar distribution of the Southern Elephant Seal includes most of the sub-Antarctic islands, for example South Georgia, the Falklands, Kerguelen, Macquarie, Campbell, Tristan da Cunha, Crozet, St Paul and Amsterdam, as well as the Antarctic mainland. The largest breeding colony, of about 300,000 seals, is on South Georgia, and there are colonies of about 100,000 at Kerguelen and Macquarie. The remainder of the total world population of between 600,000 and 700,000 are scattered over the other islands.

The distribution of the Southern Elephant Seal has not always been as widespread as it is today, for many breeding colonies were nearly exterminated when commercial sealing was at its height. Since the end of uncontrolled hunting the species has been extending its range, and present evidence suggests that recolonisation of former breeding grounds is taking place.

Early historical records

An early account of the species was given by George, Lord Anson, the commander of three ships of the Navy on a circumnavigation of the world lasting from 1740 to 1744. In his account of the party's visit to Juan Fernandez Anson states that 'Goat's flesh . . . being scarce, we rarely being able to kill above one a day; and our people growing tired of fish, . . . they at last condescended to eat seals' (Philippi fur seals) 'which by degrees they came to relish, and called it lamb. The seal, numbers of which haunt this island, hath been so often described by former writers that it is unnecessary to say anything in particular about them in this place. But there is another amphibious creature to be met here, called a sea-lyon,' (obviously an Elephant Seal from the engraving accompanying the account) 'that bears some resemblance to a seal, though it is much larger. This too we eat under the denomination of beef.' Anson then gives a remarkable and accurate account of the life and habits of the 'sea-lyon' of Juan Fernandez.

Appearance and description

A male Elephant Seal may be as much as 20 feet long and weigh 8,000 pounds. The adult bull has a dark bluish-grey coat which lightens down the flanks to a pale grey underneath the body. The females and pups have darker brownish-grey coats. the underparts being lighter than the back, and the female has a lighter neck. After a moult, the new coat is generally darker than the old, but this gradually lightens. The absence of underfur, and the presence of short, stiff hairs, give the pelt a rough texture.

The Elephant Seals gain their name not only from their immense size, but also from the trunk-like proboscis of the males. This trunk is discernible in two year old males, but is not fully developed until the males are at least eight years old, when it is long enough to overhang the mouth. The trunk, wider at the distal end and terminating in a pair of nostrils, is really an over-developed nose. It is crossed by two wrinkles, one just in front of the eyes, and the other at the point where the trunk starts to curve down. Between the wrinkles, within the trunk, and divided by a septum, is an inflatable chamber which is no more than an enlargement of the normal nasal cavity. Outside the breeding season the proboscis remains flaccid and relatively small, but when the bulls are in rut it is erected by a combination of muscular control, inflation and influx of blood. The female lacks a well-developed trunk.

The function of the trunk is not clear, but it is assumed to be in part a resonating chamber, since the roar of an Elephant Seal can be heard for several miles.

Elephant Seals have fewer teeth than any other species of the Pinnipedia except the Walrus. The upper jaw of the adult bears four incisors, two canines, eight pre-molars, and two molars, while the lower jaw has two fewer incisors. All the teeth have small enamel-covered crowns and large simple roots, and, with the exception of the canines, are probably functionless. The molar teeth in the upper jaw are often rudimentary.

The claws are greatly reduced in the forelimbs and are completely absent from the hindlimbs. Lengthening of the first and fifth digits of the hind flippers gives them a two-pronged appearance.

Habitat and habits

To obtain their food, which is mainly fish, cuttlefish and other cephalopods, Elephant Seals dive to considerable depths, perhaps as much as 2,000 feet. They can remain submerged for more than ten minutes, and their very large eyes allow the maximum amount of light to enter at great depths.

Parasites are endemic; the stomach is normally infested with nematodes, thorny-headed worms, and tape-worms, which must increase the necessary size of the Elephant Seal's meal. Acarines are found in the nasal passages, and lice in the skin, particularly in the hind flippers of the pups. In an attempt to combat the troublesome skin parasites, soothe the irritation caused by a dry skin when on land, and possibly also to keep off the sunlight, the Elephant Seals throw sand and shingle over their backs with their fore flippers, resulting in the accumulation of a pile on one side. The mobile fore flippers are also used to scratch itching parts of the body.

Southern Elephant Seals have few natural enemies. Killer Whales and Leopard Seals kill a few pups, but their greatest enemy is man, of whom they display little fear, allowing him to approach as close as he wishes (or dares).

In calm water, Elephant Seals have the habit of lying quite still with their heads and hind flippers clear of the water, but they can move with speed and agility if necessary. Over level, hard snow, they can reach a speed of 5 m.p.h., but cannot maintain it, having to stop for breath. They take a deep breath inwards, close their nostrils for a minute or so, and then exhale forcibly with a snort, often covering the muzzle with mucous. Sometimes they breath with only one nostril open, giving the face a bizarre expression.

During the spring breeding season and the summer moult the seals stay at the breeding grounds, but during the winter they take to the sea and wander around the edge of the Antarctic ice pack. On land they are extremely vocal, both bulls and cows roaring continuously, while the pups complete the cacophony with dog-like yelps.

Seasonal movements

True migration does not occur, the only seasonal movement being that during the winter, when the animals keep just ahead of the advancing pack ice.

Reproduction

The males begin to arrive at the breeding beaches at the beginning of August and are followed about a fortnight later by the first of the cows, although the majority do not arrive until the very end of the month. The breeding season lasts until October. To the accompaniment of loud roars and fierce fighting, the bulls establish their territories before the cows arrive. The fights are seldom fatal, but often cause terrible wounds, even to the loss of eyes, A lack of sensitivity to pain is a characteristic of the pinnipeds, and the bulls appear to be untroubled by these injuries. It is not known whether there is a real lack of nervous sensitivity or whether it is a question of mental attitude, but whatever the cause, this is clearly a valuable adaptation.

The fights, although savage, appear to follow definite rules. Combat begins with a roar from the challenger. If this is answered, he roars again, adopts a threatening attitude, and the battle begins. The pattern seems to be that the bull defending his territory and cows normally wins, and so the harem bull is usually able to drive off an intruder, even one much larger than himself. The cows also fight vigorously amongst themselves during the breeding season.

The cows begin to pup about a week after their arrival at the breeding ground, and the last do not give birth until October. Copulation follows about three weeks after the birth. The gestation period is in the region of 350 days. The non-harem and subordinate bulls wander around the edges of the harems copulating with the cows when the opportunities arise. The younger mature females do not come ashore, but patrol the waters surrounding the breeding grounds, and are served by these non-harem bulls.

The cows suckle their pups for about three weeks before returning to the sea to break their fast. During the lactation period a cow may lose a considerable amount of weight, while the pups are gaining about 20 pounds a day towards the end of the period. The brief but concentrated lactation is probably an adaptation to a harsh climate, and contrasts with the much longer lactation of the Northern Elephant Seal. The bulls, by this time much less aggressive, follow the cows to the sea when the pups have been weaned, and begin to feed after their long fast.

Birth to maturity

At birth, the pup has a thick woolly coat of black fur and may be up to 4 feet in length and weigh 80 pounds. During the short suckling period the pup gains a foot in length and up to 300 pounds in weight, owing to the very high fat content (about 80 per cent) of the milk produced by the cow. For about a month after weaning the pups take in no food and live on their blubber. They move to the back of the rookery, where they gather in groups, sleeping and playing for a couple of weeks before moving towards the shore. There they lie in the mud wallows to soothe the irritation of their first moult. This moult begins three weeks to a month after birth, and the woolly coat is shed first from the back and belly, and then from the head, revealing a light grey, silky coat, which stiffens to the adult texture by the end of the first year. Once the moult is completed, the pups start to feed, first on small crustaceans, and then by stages to the full adult diet.

Some time during the months of December, January, and February the adults come on land to moult. The process takes up to forty days and is patchy, leaving large strips of hair and skin littering the beaches. The adults, like the pups, lie in the mud wallows to ease their irritation. When the moult is complete, the seals return to the sea and spend the Antarctic winter months feeding.

Mortality is high among the pups, and as many as half may die during their first year. The commonest causes of death are starvation following the loss of the mother early in the season, and being crushed by a big bull. Another, less common cause of death may be a sudden cold spell following a period of sunny weather. During the sunny weather the snow under the pup gradually melts, and the pup sinks into a pit. With the coming of the cold weather the pup is trapped by frozen walls and dies of starvation.

By the end of their first year, the pups have normally reached the length of 6 feet. The age of sexual maturity seems to depend on the environment. On South Georgia, where there has been considerable exploitation of the Elephant Seal population, the females are sexually mature at 2 years of age, and the males at 4 years. On Macquarie, where the conditions are more natural, maturity is not reached until the 4th or 5th year in females, and 5 years for males. The average life span of a female is 12 years (during which time she bears about seven pups), and that of the male 24 years.

The species in relation to man

In the years immediately following the discovery of South Georgia in 1775 by Cook as he voyaged around the world, the Elephant Seals were not troubled by man. Men hunted on the island, but only for the Fur Seals which were abundant there. As these were wiped out, it was the Elephant Seals' turn, and by the middle of the nineteenth century the slaughter was in full swing. They were hunted for their oil only, as their pelts were useless; but, true to pattern, by 1900 so few Elephant Seals remained that their hunting had become profitless.

The Elephant Seal is the classic example of an animal which may to all intents and purposes be dead, but just will not lie down. Harrison Matthews in his book *Sea Elephant* cites the case of one from which all the blubber had been removed; this blind, bloody and tattered carcass lurched to its feet and made off towards the sea. Sealers have been bitten by seals similarly left for dead, and in fact it is not safe to assume an Elephant Seal dead until it has been drained of the greater part of its blood. Anson states that they are 'very full of blood, for if they are deeply wounded in a dozen places they will instantly gush out as many fountains of blood, spouting to a considerable distance.' Anson measured the volume of blood in an Elephant Seal and found 'besides what remained in the vessels, which to be sure was considerable, we got at least two hogs-heads' (about 105 gallons). For this reason hunters sever the carotid arteries before beginning work on the carcass.

The seals are driven to the shore before slaughter, to minimise transport difficulties, and are then shot through the palate as they turn at the water's edge to roar defiance at their pursuers; the bullet thus enters the brain and death is certain. As the seal dies its eyes relax and turn green due to the peculiar reflecting properties of the retina.

The blubber is removed in eight pieces. The animal is first cut along the sides, near the ground, with the sharp flenser's knives, then across the head, then across the body in front of the hind flippers, and finally across the middle of the back, both crossways and lengthways. This releases four pieces of blubber which are pulled from the carcass with steel hooks. The body is then rolled over, and the process repeated on the ventral surface. The sealers then perforate the eight pieces of blubber so that they can be threaded together on a line and pulled out to the factor ship. Hunting methods have changed little since sealing began, but in the early years blubber was more often melted down in 'trying pots' on the beaches. The oil is at present used in the manufacture of edible fats.

When sealing stopped in the late nineteenth century the stocks of Southern Elephant Seal began to recover, and today the industry is steady but controlled. Since 1910 a licensing system has been used on South Georgia which divides the coastline into four sections, only three of which are used for hunting in any one year, on a strict rota and under a rigid quota. Sealing is legal at any time except during the annual moult, but it is practicable only in September and October. The present quota allows for the killing of 6,000 seals a year. The highest number taken in modern times during a single year was in 1951 when 7,877 seals were killed, since a higher quota was then in force. Under existing regulations only large bulls (over 10 feet 6 inches long) may be taken. Each of these in good condition yields nearly a 100 gallons of oil.

The species in captivity

Most of the Elephant Seals in European zoos have been of the species *Mirounga leonina*. Some have lived as long as fifteen years in captivity. The first to be put on show in Europe was at Carl Hagenbeck's Tierpark at Stellingen in 1910. Subsequently the London Zoo acquired a Southern Elephant Seal in 1911, and two more in 1914. After the first World War and before the second the Hagenbecks imported a total of two dozen. Several young were born to these animals in captivity, but most were stillborn and none survived their first few hours. The reason for this failure is unexplained.

The most famous of the captive Elephant Seals was 'Goliath', the first adult male to arrive at Stellingen. He came in 1926 and weighed in at 4,821 pounds, packed into a body 16 feet 6 inches in length. His normal daily diet was 100 pounds of fish, but he is recorded as having once eaten as much as 385 pounds in a day. He was sold to the Ringling Brothers Circus in 1928, and spent several apparently healthy years travelling with them. In the winter of 1933–34 he was temporarily housed in the Philadelphia Zoo, and by that time he had grown another 6 inches in length and more than half a ton in weight.

At the present time the Philadelphia Zoo possesses another Southern Elephant Seal, christened 'Goliath II', but not of such imposing proportions as his namesake. He is a mere 11 feet long, but manages to eat 60 pounds of assorted fish a day. He rejects squids in favour of fish, which is against the accepted knowledge of the food preferences of the species, and his appetite when moulting is only half that at other times. In warm weather he throws water over his back with his flippers, just as his wild brethren throw up sand. A Southern Elephant Seal can be seen in Britain at Edinburgh Zoo.

THE NORTHERN ELEPHANT SEAL (Plate 8)   *Mirounga angustirostris*

Distribution and population

At the present time the Northern Elephant Seal is found only on the Santa Barbara Islands and Los Coronados off the Californian coast, and on Guadalupe, San Geronimo, and San Benito off the coasts of Mexican Lower California.

Individuals have been seen from time to time as far north as British Columbia and, very exceptionally, Prince of Wales Island, Alaska. There are breeding colonies on Guadalupe, San Geronimo and in the Santa Barbara group on San Miguel and San Nicholas. The total population of the species is between 10,000 and 15,000.

Early historical records

At the beginning of the nineteenth century the range was more extensive, and rookeries were plentiful from San Francisco Bay southwards for nearly a thousand miles. These rookeries were wiped out by the activity of hunters, and at the turn of the century fewer than 100 individuals of the entire species remained. The existing population are all descendants of these few animals, to which protection came just in time.

Appearance and description

In general appearance the Northern Elephant Seal resembles the Southern, although it is usually smaller. Whereas adult males of the Southern species may be 20 feet in length, it is rare for the Northern to exceed 16. The skull of the Northern Elephant Seal is usually narrower, but in parts more heavily built, that that of its southern counterpart. The one characteristic in which the Northern surpasses the Southern is in the size of its trunk. The proboscis is so long that in the adult male it may hang down in front of the mouth for a foot or more. When erected it curves down into the mouth and its tip is directed down the throat. Across the snout is a deep transverse groove. Whether flaccid or in use this appendage gives the seal a unique appearance.

The coat is dark grey when freshly moulted, but instead of fading with time tends to become a yellowish-brown colour.

Habitat and habits

The annual moult begins in May, but the older members of the herd tend to moult later in the year than the younger, and some are still moulting in July. The hair, and some of the superficial skin, is shed in patches, which gives the seals a piebald appearance.

G

When at sea the Northern Elephant Seal is lively and agile in spite of its bulk. It is a strong swimmer, sculling with the very large hind flippers and using its front flippers only for steering and balance. It has been observed swimming at 12 m.p.h. and can probably travel much faster when necessary. When swimming at this speed near the surface it sends up a bow wave a foot high, making it easy for an observer to follow its movements. Such a large animal has few enemies in the water, but youngsters have been recorded as showing signs of shark bites.

Individuals have been seen resting in the water near the shore, both at the surface and on the sea bottom. They seem able to alter their buoyancy at will, and it appears that this is done by regulating the amount of air left in the respiratory system when they exhale, and then closing their nostrils.

While searching for food the Elephant Seal descends to deep water. The stomach of one Northern Elephant Seal which was examined contained 7 rat-fish, a Californian dogfish, a puffer-shark, 3 skates, and 4 squid. All these animals are fairly slow swimmers and inhabit deep waters. Rat-fish are never found in less than 50 fathoms and most of the Elephant Seal's prey is probably taken at this depth or below. The rudimentary nature of all the seal's teeth except the canines indicates that food is swallowed without mastication. This may be one reason for the enormous length of the gut in these seals. The record for the pinnipeds is held by an Elephant Seal which had a gut 662 feet in length — one-eighth of a mile, or half the distance round a running track.

When at sea the Northern Elephant Seal is a solitary creature, wandering by itself. It also leaves the beaches as an individual and not as a member of a herd.

Its mobility and solitary habits at sea are in marked contrast to behaviour on land. Progress ashore is slow and clumsy, a caterpillar-like movement, using the fore flippers and the pelvic region to draw the belly forward by hunching the back, and leaving the hind flippers to drag uselessly behind. It is not surprising that for most of the time the seals are on land they remain either asleep or inert. Even outside the breeding season they spend much time ashore, and when hauled out they are strongly gregarious. Their instincts lead them to come into actual bodily contact with each other, and it is a common sight to see Elephant Seals squashed together even on an otherwise deserted beach.

The phlegmatic temperament of the species has been a source of wonder to all those who have observed it at first hand. Out of the breeding season even the bulls are placid, and very little fighting or bickering takes place. If a human intrudes on the hauling grounds, they show little sign of having been disturbed, and although some may make their way in a leisurely fashion to the edge of the water, about half appear to have noticed nothing unusual. During the breeding season the indifference of the adult bulls to man is absolute; they may be approached to within 3 or 4 feet with complete impunity, and with no sign of concern from the seals. Females and young bulls are not quite so immovable, but they do no more than threaten and move out of the immediate vicinity of the invader. Sleeping Elephant Seals are very hard to waken, and it has been possible for zoologists to measure respiratory rhythms, rectal temperature, and heart beat of the slumbering beasts. Pulse rates have even been recorded from animals lying awake.

This extreme complacency could only have evolved in such an animal as the Elephant Seal, breeding for hundreds of generations on remote islands with nothing to fear from land carnivores, the only animals which could have challenged its supremacy. This attitude was no handicap to the species before the arrival of man in quest of oil, when the inherent tameness of the seals proved their undoing, and nearly resulted in their extinction.

A characteristic of these seals on land is their periodic suspension of breathing. While lying asleep they may breathe regularly for five minutes, taking about five breaths a minute, and then stop breathing for about five minutes. Like Southern Elephant Seals they often throw loose sand over their backs with their fore flippers; they are not fond of being washed by waves, and as the tide comes up the beach they will move further inland.

They form a noisy community; even when lying at ease they produce a steady chorus of loud coughs, sneezes, snorts, grunts, and yawns. Besides these sounds, there are true vocalisations which have a social significance. The characteristic sound is a resonant snort, and is made by both sexes, but is at its deepest and loudest uttered as a threat by the adult males. Young males and cows usually threaten with a wide open mouth and a gurgling choking sound, sometimes replaced by a whining note. When an adult male utters his snorting threat he rears up so that his muzzle is vertical; the proboscis is inflated and curves round so that it nearly touches the roof of the mouth and points down the throat. The whole pharynx can then be employed as a resonator to magnify the snort from the proboscis. The sound is like a metallic clapping, and is produced in bursts of

10 to 15 'claps', at a rate of about 4 per second. Some authorities believe the clapping may originate from the fluttering of cartilaginous flaps in the proboscis, although others deny this and point out that the flaps are valves to keep the water out of the proboscis while the animal is swimming. The noise, however it is produced, is extremely loud, and can be heard over a distance of half a mile, and above the noise of the surf and the rookery.

Other sounds, usually uttered by animals being pushed around or trodden on by their larger kin, include whimpering, and yapping like that of a dog.

Although the seals are usually pacific, occasional scuffles do break out. They lie alongside and touching one another quite amicably, but when one becomes restless he may disturb his neighbour and a contest for position may develop, both seals rearing up and trying to bring the weight of their heads and forequarters down on the opponent in order to get the upper position. Sometimes the squabble results in the retreat of one seal for a few feet; more often, after a moment or two of posturing, both disengage and subside once more into sleep alongside one another. The youngsters, and occasionally even the adults, play chasing games in the water, and love to surf-ride. Few Elephant Seals show interest in inanimate objects but some have been seen tossing seaweed as if playing with it.

The gregarious instincts of the Northern Elephant Seal are so strong that if there are none of their own species available they will wedge themselves in among groups of the Californian Sealion, which share the same islands. Except during the breeding season, it is quite a common sight to see mixed aggregations of sealions and seals. The two species take one another quite calmly, and each treats the other more or less as if it were one of its fellows. Several sealions may sometimes be seen asleep on the back of one Elephant Seal, a much softer and warmer bed than the beach. Ashore the sealion is the more agile and has less to fear, but in the water they avoid getting too close to the seals. It is, however, sometimes possible for a bull sealion to dominate a bull Elephant Seal several time his size. Once or twice male sealions have been seen to challenge and rear up in front of a similarly threatening Elephant Seal and the seal has been the one to withdraw. This observation was made at the beginning of the sealion breeding season, but it indicates that the Californian Sealion cannot invariably be afraid of something taller than itself.

Cormorants and American Western Gulls (*Larus occidentalis*) are found near the mixed herds of sealion and seal, and it has been suggested that this association is of mutual advantage. The sensitive gulls take fright at any disturbance, even several hundred yards away, and take off, alerting the cormorants which have a smaller flight distance, and then if these take off in a rush they alarm the seals and sealions. Normally only the sealions take advantage of the early warning system and take to the water; the seals remain unperturbed. In return for the warning system the pinnipeds probably afford protection for the birds against predators such as foxes, which may raid nests, and it has been noticed that dogs are afraid of seals.

Seasonal movements

There is no migratory movement, but in the spring all the adult bulls are away at sea feeding, and are said to travel mainly southwards.

Reproduction

The mating behaviour of the Northern Elephant Seal resembles that of the Southern species. The breeding season is from December to March, and at the beginning of the period the adult bulls take up their positions on the beaches and become belligerent towards other males. The dominant bulls are concerned not so much with collecting a harem as with maintaining their position on the beach among the hauled-out cows. Cows mate, or are forced to mate, indiscriminately; the bulls do not try to keep individual cows but to stay in a situation where many cows are available. On the breeding portion of the beach the ratio of dominant bulls to cows is about one to thirteen.

Fighting is commonplace, but many contests are won without a blow struck. Dominant bulls often maintain their supremacy simply by giving the vocal challenge. It is noticeable that most of the fights are between subordinate males, and even in the middle of the breeding season dominant bulls seldom have fresh scars or wounds.

Fighting when it does occur may be extremely bloody. The males rear up and face each other with heads in the air and chests almost touching. Each strikes downwards and tries to grip his opponent with his teeth and shake him. If one loses his grip he rears up and strikes again. All the time he is careful to keep chest and shoulders, with their tough shield of bare hide, facing the opponent. While fighting, the proboscis is withdrawn. Many fights are inconclusive, but if one flees, he must expose his more vulnerable flanks, where most of the worst wounds are received. On the whole, the ritual character of the fight prevents many fatalities, and mortal wounds are exceedingly rare. Fights may be carried into the water, and turn the sea blood-red for yards around, but seemingly with little inconvenience to the combatants.

The cows mate while still lactating and, unlike the Southern Elephant Seals, go to the sea to feed during this time.

Birth to maturity

The exact period of lactation is not known but it is certain that the pups are independent of their mothers' milk three months after birth in December or January. Not for some weeks after their birth do the youngsters enter the water.

The pup is just under 4 feet long at birth, with a curly, very dark grey coat, which is moulted after about 8 weeks to the normal adult coat. The lifespan is about 20 years, but the mortality rate of the youngsters is high, due to the carelessness of the big adult bulls.

The species in relation to man

Commercial hunting of the Elephant Seals off the coast of America started in 1818 and continued unabated until the 1860s when the species had become so reduced that it was no longer worth the search. The hunters had been aided by the co-operation of the lethargic seals, who took practically no evasive action. The sealers would get between their quarry and the sea, and drive the seals further inland, where they were killed with muskets, lances, and sealing clubs. At this point panic would sometimes break out among the Elephant Seals, and they would obligingly crush some of their companions in the melée and save the hunters the price of ammunition. The harvest, while it lasted, was simple and plentiful. A big bull killed by the crew of the brig *Mary Helen* in 1852 gave 210 gallons of oil. With large catches and yields of this order it is not surprising that sealing was profitable.

By 1880 only one small herd was known to exist. A further 294 were killed between that date and 1885, but after this they were believed to be extinct. In 1907, however, a herd was found at Guadalupe, on a small beach backed by cliffs 3,000 feet high. There were probably less than 100 of them, but 14 were killed and sent as specimens to museums.

This small herd, as far as is known, was the nucleus from which all the Northern Elephant Seals alive today descended.

In 1911 the Mexican Government gave the seals partial protection and in 1922 total immunity.

The species in captivity

The earliest record of a Northern Elephant Seal in captivity is that of five young ones that went to live in Philadelphia Zoo in 1882, but these did not survive for long.

No more specimens were kept in zoos until New York Zoo obtained some in 1911. Since the 1920s San Diego has nearly always had Northern Elephant Seals on show, (in fact the symbol of the San Diego Zoo is a picture of the head and neck of a Northern Elephant Seal), but their lifespan in captivity is poor compared to that of the Southern species, and the longest-lived has survived no more than five years.

In temperature range they seem hardy, for three specimens sent to Copenhagen in 1953 survived temperatures of 12 degrees Centigrade without apparent ill-effect. This is far below anything they would naturally encounter, but the only noticeable change in their behaviour was that they moved into the water to sleep.

THE BLADDERNOSE OR HOODED SEAL (Plate 8)   *Cystophora cristata*

Distribution and population

The Bladdernose or Hooded Seal is an inhabitant of the northern Atlantic and Arctic Seas. Members of the species rarely frequent dry land or even solid ice, but are found in deep waters and on floating ice floes, which has made it quite difficult to determine their numbers. The world population is, however, estimated at between 300,000 and 500,000, distributed from Bear Island west of Norway, to Spitzbergen, southwards to Jan Mayen and Iceland, westwards to southern Greenland, and then spreading as far as Newfoundland, along the eastern coasts of Labrador, and throughout Baffin Bay. Stragglers have been recorded much further afield, and there have been sightings off Florida, and in the Bay of Biscay. One was seen in the River Orwell in Suffolk on 29th June 1847.

Appearance and description

In length the sexes differ very little, the bulls attaining lengths of up to 11 feet 6 inches, the cows about 9 inches less. But the sexes may be easily distinguished by their relative bulks, for the adult males weigh up to 900 pounds whereas the females are no more than 500 to 600 pounds. Apart from this difference in bulk, the sexes may be separated by differences in colour and marking. The adult bulls are a bluish-grey colour above, paling along the flanks to light grey on the ventral surface. Some individuals are marked with lighter spots all over the surface of the body, while others display darker blotches. The cows are generally paler than the bulls and the markings are much less distinct. Both sexes have very dark grey, almost black, faces and muzzles, and like their relatives the Elephant Seals have an inflatable proboscis, much more pronounced in the male, but in this seal it takes the form of a 'hood' on top of the head, reaching right back above and behind the eyes and forward to the muzzle. The hood, which is an enlargement of the nasal cavity, is very elastic and muscular and may be inflated with air.

Habitat and habits

Bladdernose Seals spend most of their time swimming in deep waters, where they are continually active and extremely accomplished performers. When swimming at the surface they keep very low in the water, and only the tops of their heads are visible. The seals swim along the sea bottom, where they are believed to feed upon echinoderms and other invertebrates, and also near the surface, where fish and cephalopods are the probable prey. The diet is uncertain, as the only time that the animals can be killed for examination is at the breeding season, or during the moult, when they do not feed.

The species has few enemies, although Polar Bears have been known to attack both the young and adult seals. Man is, as usual, the greatest enemy with which they have to contend.

It is said that the hood is inflated when the animal is frightened or excited but this has still to be proved. A phenomenon which may be attributed to the emotions, however, is that shown most often by bulls, who are not very tolerant of one another. A large, bright red bladder may suddenly be forced out of the left nostril of the animal. This bladder is formed by the inflation of a very elastic portion of the inter-nasal septum, and it is presumed to be blown out of the nostril with air which has been previously taken into the stomach, and forced into the hood with closed nostrils.

Seasonal movements

The seasonal movements are not fully understood, but for the most part they appear to be closely associated with the breeding and moulting times. For most of the year the seals are solitary and widely scattered, but there does seem to be some concentration around Greenland during June and July when they pass through a period of moulting. As the winter approaches the animals disperse again to their unknown winter feeding grounds. In early spring they begin to gather on the breeding grounds, around Jan Mayen and north of Newfoundland. In these areas widely scattered family groups can be distinguished, each consisting of a bull, a cow, and a pup. Due to the differing climates of the two regions the aggregation around Newfoundland disperses earlier in the year than that around Jan Mayen, and the impression is of one aggregation increasing as the other decreases. After breeding, the Jan Mayen seals go northwards to Spitzbergen, whilst the Newfoundland aggregation move up to the Greenland ice.

Reproduction

Bladdernose Seals are often seen in the same areas as Harp Seals, and it is known that they both breed in the same regions. The two species remain separate, and the Bladdernose forms family groups on floating ice floes.

The bull and the cow haul out on to the floe during March, and the pup is born soon after. The pup is suckled for two or three weeks only, and then, after lactation has ceased, the adults return to the sea. The pup remains behind for a further two weeks before following the example of its parents by taking to the water and heading northwards.

Birth to maturity

At birth the pup is about 3 feet 6 inches in length, 30 pounds in weight, and is covered with a silvery-blue coat on the back, which is in strong contrast with the much lighter cream coloured fur on the undersurface of the body. The pups are often called 'blue-backs', and are the principal targets of the seal hunters. Once the pup has taken to the water it remains solitary until it is sexually mature at around four years of age. Although these seals are solitary and independent there is reason to believe that outside the breeding season the sexes occupy different areas. If one came across a group of Bladdernose Seals, even though they were scattered over a wide area, it is fairly certain that they would be found to be all of one sex.

The species in relation to man

As the Bladdernose Seals and the Harp Seals breed at the same time of year and in the same areas they have received the simultaneous attention of hunters, although the Bladdernose normally breeds on floes further away from the mainland.

Although they prefer the Harp Seal skin for use in the building of their kayaks (as the skin of the Bladdernose Seal is rather porous) the Eskimos are very fond of the Bladdernose's flesh which they regard as something of a delicacy.

At the present time sealing agreements are in force which cover both the Harp and Bladdernose Seals. Hunting of the Bladdernose is limited to a one month period between June 10th and July 10th, and once an area has been visited it may not be culled again in the same year.

The species in captivity

Bladdernose Seals have been kept with only a limited amount of success in zoos, few surviving for more than eighteen months. Only four individuals are at present in captivity. Cologne, Hamburg, and Berlin Zoos each have a male specimen, and the only female in captivity is in the New York Aquarium.

7. Seals of the Antarctic

THE LEOPARD SEAL (Plate 9)   *Hydrurga leptonyx*

Distribution and population

The Leopard Seal is often described as a menace to the other animals that inhabit the Antarctic and sub-Antarctic seas. It is certainly the only seal which regularly takes warm-blooded prey, and the sealions, fur seals and true seals of the southern hemisphere may lose some of their pups to this predatory relative.

The species is quite abundant (at least 200,000) and inhabits not only the pack ice of the Antarctic but regions further afield, from the sub-Antarctic islands to Australia, New Zealand, Cape Horn, Tasmania, Patagonia and Kerguelen. It is often sighted, but apart from a winter population of up to 1000 on Heard Island, it is rare to see more than one or two individuals together. Evidence accumulated over the years indicates that Leopard Seals are solitary, range widely (especially the younger animals), and are never common in any one locality.

Early historical records

The species was first named and described by D. de Blainville in 1820, from specimens obtained from the vicinity of the Falklands. The name he assigned to the species was *Phoca leptonyx*.

Appearance and description

Unlike most of the world's mammals, the female Leopard Seal is larger than the male. The adult bull Leopard Seal attains a length of up to 10 feet, but the adult cow may grow as much as 2 feet longer. Externally, however, there is very little other difference between the sexes. The back is dark grey in colour, with lighter spots, shading down the flanks to a light grey undersurface marked with darker spots.

The body is long and narrow, and bears a very large and powerful head and neck. The snout is bluntly rounded, and the mouth is enormous, with a very snake-like gape. Many observers have commented on the reptilian appearance of this seal.

The teeth have three long pointed cusps — a characteristic feature especially noticeable in the cheek teeth. The central cusp is long and curved backwards, and the shorter outer pair are curved inwards towards each other.

Habitat and general habits

Although itself a fearsome predator the Leopard Seal, like other pinnipeds, has every reason to fear the Killer Whale. But unlike other pinnipeds the Leopard Seal has no other enemies.

Leopard Seals feed on fish, cephalopods, penguins and young seals, and will even scavenge on the carcasses of large marine mammals such as whales. They lie in wait for penguins on the ice floes, snapping at them when they take to the water. Their appetites are considerable. Twenty-eight pounds of fish were found in the stomach of one specimen captured, and a complete 3 feet long penguin in another. Occasionally they will even eat sea plants. Dr Frederick Knox reported to James Gray that he had examined the stomach content of a killed Leopard Seal and had discovered '. . . numerous fish bones, a few feathers, and considerable portions of a pale green, broad-leaved marine Fucus.' He also noted that 'thousands of small, hard, round whiteworms (parasitical) pervaded all parts of the intestines.'

After feeding, Leopard Seals haul out on pack ice or floes and sleep. They appear to have difficulty in getting out of the water on to a floe using their flippers. Harrison Matthews describes how one animal moved off some distance, then turned, swam at great speed towards the floe, and shot out of the water like a torpedo to land right on top of the ice.

Once on land they are ungainly and quite unable to use their flippers for locomotion. They move forward with a looping action, using the chest and hind end of the body.

Leopard Seals like to investigate any unusual phenomenon, such as the activities of man. Their vocal repertoire is limited, but if they are disturbed from their sleep they will emit a few whistles, and what some writers have described as 'subdued chuckling'.

Seasonal movements

The Leopard Seal does not migrate. Whilst many of the animals keep to the outer edges of the pack ice during the winter, others remain on the firm ice to the south, and still others stay near the sub-Antarctic islands such as South Georgia, St Paul and Macquarie.

Reproduction

The breeding habits of the species are not known but it is assumed that mating occurs on the ice after lactation has ceased. The small amount of evidence available suggests that the pups are born between November and December, that lactation continues for about eight weeks, and that mating therefore takes place during January or February. It is thought that the blastocyst implants almost immediately.

Birth to maturity

Judging from the few pups that have ever been seen, the infant Leopard Seal is quite large at birth — 5 feet or more in length and over 60 pounds in weight. The coat is thick, soft, and light grey in colour. The body is long and thin, with a very large head — almost a miniature of the parent.

When lactation stops the pups start to take solid food in the form of small fish, and possibly crustaceans and cephalopods, and then become completely independent of the adults.

Nobody knows at what age the pup passes through its post-natal moult, but some zoologists suggest that the moult occurs whilst the pup is still suckling.

The species in relation to man

Leopard Seals have never been seen often enough, or in sufficient numbers, for man to even consider hunting them on a commercial scale. In spite of their ferocious reputation there seems to be no evidence of unprovoked attacks upon man.

The species in captivity

The Leopard Seal fares poorly in captivity and few zoos have attempted to keep them. Hagenbeck's Tierpark at Stellingen in Germany managed to keep one for two years, and there were once a few living in Taronga Zoo, Sydney, Australia.

THE WEDDELL SEAL (Plate 9)   *Leptonychotes weddellii*

Distribution and estimated population

The Weddell Seal is the most southerly of the Antarctic seals and lives almost invariably within sight of the Antarctic mainland in both summer and winter, though a few individuals occasionally venture as far afield as South Australia, New Zealand, Macquarie, Kerguelen, Heard, the Falklands and Juan Fernandez. They are frequently seen off the South Orkneys, and breed (although in very small numbers) on South Georgia. The world population of the species is estimated to be between 200,000 and 500,000.

Early historical records

James Weddell, during his 'voyage to the South Pole' in the years 1822 to 1824, captured six seals in January, 1823. He made a drawing of one and captioned it *Sea Leopard of South Orkneys*. This drawing, which has since been described, unkindly but frankly, as 'a cartoon', is undoubtedly the first illustration of a Weddell Seal. Since that date the species has been seen regularly by the members of Antarctic expeditions.

Appearance and description

The Weddell Seal is a large and tubby beast weighing up to 900 pounds, and like the Leopard Seal the female is usually larger than the male. Males measure up to 10 feet, and females up to 11 feet. In colour the Weddell Seal is dark grey above and very light grey below, with light blotches and streaks over the whole body. The face is small, with very large, rich brown eyes, and the muzzle bears a bunch of stiff, light-brown, tapering whiskers each side of the snout.

Habitat and general habits

The Weddell Seal feeds mainly on cephalopods, crustaceans and fish, together with a certain amount of mud, sand and stones. Some zoologists have stated that the Weddell Seal eats only three times its own weight of food per year, which is equivalent to about a ton of fish and cephalopods. This is a very small amount of food for such a large animal in such cold surroundings, but perhaps the estimate was based on the contents of the stomachs of animals killed during a period when they were not feeding regularly, possibly during or shortly after the breeding season.

When the weather is really cold the seals take to the water, where the temperature is warmer and more constant, but during the spring and summer they are quite happy to laze on top of the ice in small scattered groups, lying on their sides, or on their backs, sleeping restlessly with their heads drawn into the rolls of blubber round the neck. Their slumber is punctuated by much scratching, yawning, gurgling and fidgeting, and if they are disturbed by man, who has to shout long and hard to rouse the sleeping beasts, they will look at the intruder with a nonplussed, vacant, unbelieving expression. The first indication of anxiety by the seal is the emptying of its bladder, and this is followed by a series of hisses, moans, and piping noises. The animal then moves off clumsily, without the aid of its flippers, to a crack in the ice, or a blow hole, near which it always lies in case of emergency.

To make a blow hole the seal embeds its lower incisors and canines in the ice, either from above or below, and then revolves its upper incisors and canines in an arc until the hole is cut. This process puts strain on the teeth, which are subjected to a great deal of wear and tear and in older animals may be very badly worn.

Weddell Seals spend the winter *under* the ice, where they maintain their blow holes or construct new ones, or use the natural ventilated domes which occur frequently in the ice. Many Antarctic explorers have heard the seals scratching and calling to each other under the ice throughout the long winter months.

When the ice starts to disintegrate with the coming of summer, the seals move gradually southwards away from the open water and keep near the solid ice fringing the mainland shore.

The injured, aged and sick animals retire to some secluded spot as far away from their fellows as possible to recover or to die. The bodies of some of these animals have been discovered, often several feet under the surface of the ice and up to thirty-five miles from the coast. Some bodies have even been discovered on the surface of glaciers over 3,000 feet above sea level. This phenomenon, the urge of the unfit seal to put as much distance as possible between itself and its fellows, has been called the 'instinct of retirement', and occurs to a greater or lesser extent in a number of species of the Pinnipedia.

Seasonal movements

The species is non-migratory, movement being dependent on the food available rather than the changing of seasons and climate.

Reproduction

Breeding takes place during spring and early summer, and lasts from September until January. The cows haul out towards the beginning of September, and give birth to the pups a day or so later, after a gestation period of ten to eleven months. The birth of the pup takes about fifteen minutes, and the youngster remains attached to its mother for some time before the umbilical cord is severed. The cow does not bite through the cord, but she whips her hindquarters from side to side until the cord breaks. The arrival of the cows at the rookeries, and therefore the births of the pups, are spread over a period of two months from September to November, the majority of the pups being born during the first week of November.

The cows at first protect their offspring vigorously against other cows and human intruders, and attack fiercely. So strong is the mother Weddell's protective instinct towards her newborn pup that she sometimes stays with a youngster for several days after it has died.

The pup is suckled for about six weeks while the cow fasts and after this she is ready to mate again. The bulls arrive at the rookeries some two or three weeks after pupping has started, and between October and December fighting between them is common; they aim their slashing teeth at the genitals of their opponents, and many bulls that haul out at the breeding grounds are very badly torn.

Birth to maturity

At birth the pup is about 4 feet 6 inches long, weighs about 60 pounds, and is covered with a thick, woolly, rusty-grey coat with little or no markings. By the end of lactation the pup has gained about 200 pounds in weight; its mother, on the other hand, has lost some 300 pounds and is very thin and emaciated. At the age of two weeks, while still suckling, the pup undergoes its first moult; this lasts until the end of lactation, about three weeks, by which time the pup's coat has an adult coloration. During the period of moulting and suckling the pup often takes to the water, sometimes as soon as three or four days after birth. Once lactation ceases, the pup, which is now some 7 feet long, starts to take solid food in the form of small fish and crustaceans.

The mortality rate amongst the pups is as high as 50 per cent during the first two months. Many pups are crushed to death by the ice breaking up. The cows also kill their pups when they are being aggressive towards an intruder. Their aggression appears to become misplaced towards the defenceless pups. The cows also cause the deaths of their offspring through neglect and indifference — in stark contrast to their initial solicitude — and any pup that loses its mother quickly becomes weak and easy prey to the scavenging skuas and gulls.

The females are thought to be sexually mature and capable of breeding at three years of age, the males a year later.

The species in relation to man

A small number of Weddell Seals were killed by the men under Palmer and Powell in 1821, during a voyage which led to the discovery of South Orkneys. Otherwise man has left this species alone.

THE ROSS SEAL (Plate 9)   *Ommatophoca rossi*

Distribution and population

The Ross Seal is the least known of all the pinnipeds, even though reasonably large numbers of them (about 20,000) live all along the fringe of the Antarctic continent south of the latitude 60 degrees. The species has only rarely

H

been seen and recorded, but the records suggest that it is solitary and inhabits thick ice packs.

Early historical records

The species was discovered by Sir James Ross, the commander of the ships *Erebus* and *Terror* during the British Antarctic Expedition of 1839–43. Ross captured the first specimen on 8th January 1840. Subsequently John E. Gray described a skull with whole skin intact, together with two separate skulls, and named the new species after its discoverer. Since then the Ross Seal has rarely been seen — only fifty specimens, in fact, had been recorded up to the outbreak of the Second World War, and though it is a commoner sight now as a result of renewed interest in Antarctica over the last twenty years, zoologists have still had little opportunity to observe the creature's habits.

Appearance and description

If few specimens have been seen, even fewer have been captured and measured. The measurements that are available suggest that there is little difference in size between the sexes, and that both males and females may attain a length of up to 11 feet. In colour both sexes are a dark greenish-grey above, shading to a light grey on the chest and abdomen, with a very dark chin and throat, and with light stripes running along the flanks from the shoulders.

The body is so fat that the head, with its rather short, squashed face and pro-truding forehead, may almost disappear into the rolls of blubber of the neck. The mouth is surprisingly small, and though the eyes may *appear* to be quite small they are in fact very large. Gray, in his account of the Zoology of the *Erebus* and *Terror* voyage, refers to Ross's seal as 'larged-eyed'. In fact, the eyes bulge out of the head, and their great size enables the seal to discern food and obstacles more clearly in the dark waters under the ice.

The flippers are large and well-developed but bear only rudimentary claws which serve no useful purpose. The incisor and canine teeth are needle-like hooks, ideal for catching cephalopods. The pre-molars and molars degenerate; sometimes they remain loosely in the jaws, and sometimes they are completely absent. It is therefore only rarely that two Ross Seals are found with an identical set of teeth.

Habitat and general habits

The Ross Seal feeds mainly on cephalopods. It supplements this diet with fish and krill, and possibly nibbles at vegetable matter from time to time. No stones, grit or sand have ever been found in its stomach, but parasitic nematodes and tape-worms are common.

Ross Seals have few enemies in the Antarctic wastes, but many of them bear scars. These scars are not caused by the Killer Whale (the Ross Seal inhabits the heavy pack ice well out of the range of the whale) but may be the result of fighting during the breeding season, or of attacks by Leopard Seals.

When disturbed the Ross Seal appears to inflate a portion of its pharynx, or perhaps its soft palate, and emits a series of tremulous murmuring sounds, which are followed by clicking noises with the mouth shut, and end with a snort from the nostrils.

Seasonal movements

Not known.

Reproduction

Breeding habits, time of the breeding season, length of gestation and lactation, pupping time, and size, weight and coloration of the pups are all completely unknown.

Birth to maturity

The pup presumably moults shortly after the cessation of lactation, and the moult is thought to last two or three weeks. The adults moult during January and grow a new dark grey coat which fades slightly during the year to a greenish-grey colour. The adults fast during the period of the moult.

THE CRABEATER SEAL (Plate 14)   *Lobodon carcinophagus*

Distribution and estimated population

The Crabeater Seal is the most abundant pinniped in the world, but paradoxically it is one of the least known. Estimates of the population vary greatly but they are never less than 2,000,000, and some are as high as 5,000,000. The species frequents the entire shoreline of the Antarctic continent, and since it prefers floating ice to solid pack ice it is continually on the move — often in large groups. A few individual Crabeaters have moved very great distances and have been seen in Australia, New Zealand, and even off San Sidro, north of Buenos Aires.

Early historical records

The species was first named *Phoca carcinophaga*, by Hombron and Jacquinot in 1842, after they had seen the seal during the voyage of the ships *L'Astrolabe* and *La Zélée* to the South Pole during the years 1837 to 1840.

Appearance and description

The adults of both sexes are about the same size — up to 9 feet in length and 500 pounds in weight. The body is long and slim, and covered with a coat which changes colour during the months following the moult. Immediately after the moult the fur is a warm brownish grey colour along the back, lightening to silvery grey along the underside. Along the flanks, and the sides of the neck and shoulders, there are a number of rich brown rings. As the months pass the coat colour gradually fades until it becomes creamy white, and the Crabeater is often referred to as the 'White Seal'.

The head bears a rather long pointed snout which the animal turns up when it is excited or frightened.

Habitat and general habits

The Crabeater Seal got its name because it feeds exclusively on the crustacean Krill, and therefore does not compete seriously with other Antarctic seals. Its teeth are highly adapted and specialised for this food. The cheek teeth each bear up to five long projecting cusps arranged in a line with the jaw, the longest cusp at the midpoint of each tooth. The teeth of the lower jaw are so positioned that when the mouth closes their cusps fill the spaces between the teeth in the upper jaw. Thus the closed jaws provide an intricate straining system which can reject water, but not krill, when the seal snatches a mouthful of water in which the crustaceans are swimming. Parts of the Antarctic Ocean teem with myriad of these tiny creatures and they provide sufficient food for some of the largest whales as well as for the Crabeater and other sea creatures. Indigestible particles taken in by the seal along with the krill may serve some useful purpose in breaking up the food in the stomach. As with other seals which eat *Euphausia* (krill) the excreta are bright red.

Most of the adult seals are badly scarred, but at the beginning of the century explorers realised that the scars were of two types, and were obviously of different origins. Those on the head and neck were small and were probably caused by fighting between rival Crabeaters during the breeding season. The other type of scars were on the lower flanks and underside of the body. These scars were distinct from those of the head and neck — deep, parallel gashes up to 2 feet long that could not possibly have been caused by any species of seal. The scars were on the undersurface of the body and probably inflicted in the water from below. The culprit was almost certainly the dreaded Killer Whale.

Unlike the Weddell Seal, the Crabeater is fairly rapid over ice (at least 15 miles per hour according to one estimate) and as the body is relatively slim it is quite capable of utilising the fore flippers to lever its way along. When disturbed by man the Crabeater attacks at once with its mouth open, issuing angry hisses and husky roars. But the animal rarely goes beyond this disgruntled, bad-tempered stage; it simply turns tail and streaks off to its nearest breathing hole in the ice and plunges out of sight.

As with the Weddell Seal, the 'instinct of retirement' is strong in the old and sick animals.

Seasonal movements

The Crabeater is not truly migratory and only moves to be near its food supply around the edges of the pack ice. As this moves outwards and northwards in the winter the majority of the seals move out with it and stay near the floating ice floes. There is some evidence that a few individuals remain in the south under the ice during the winter. At the coming of summer the seals return south with the receding ice edge.

Reproduction

Little is known of the breeding habits of the Crabeater Seal. The breeding season occurs during the spring, between October and December — in the pack ice which is practically inaccessible to man. No one has ever seen these animals mate, but the testes of males captured during November have proved to be full of sperm, probably indicating that breeding time was near. The pups are believed to be born early in October on the pack ice many miles from the nearest coast, and few have ever been seen. Mating follows some weeks after the birth of the pup, and the gestation period is about nine months.

Birth to maturity

At birth the pup is covered with a thick, rough, light-brown coat, and is about 4 feet 6 inches in length. The period of lactation is uncertain; some authorities place it at five weeks, others at two weeks, and still others at only three or four days. At the end of lactation, probably between two and five weeks after birth, the pup moults. The limbs moult first, to be followed by the head, back, tail, sides and abdomen, in that order. The new coat is darker than the old but fades during the year. The adults moult during January and February but continue to feed and swim during that period.

The females are sexually mature at around two years of age, the males probably a year later.

The species in relation to man

The skins of Crabeater Seals have no commercial use; those of the adult are usually badly scarred, and the pup pelts are practically unobtainable. But explorers have killed individuals from time to time for food.

8. Seals Native to Britain

THE COMMON OR HARBOUR SEAL (Plate 11)   *Phoca vitulina*

Distribution and estimated population

The Common Seal is a very widely distributed species inhabiting coastal regions over much of the Northern Hemisphere. Its range extends from Portugal along the Atlantic coast northwards as far as Finnmark in northern Norway; westwards around the British Isles, Iceland and Greenland; further westwards to the coast of North America, into Baffin Bay and Hudson Bay, and southwards to the latitude of New York City (about 30 degrees N). The Common Seal also lives on the Pacific side of North America — from Herschel Island, north of Alaska, through the Bering Sea (including the Pribilofs and the Aleutians) and down both the western coasts of North America as far as Guadalupe and the eastern coasts of Asia from Kamchatka to Japan, Sakhalin, Korea and the Yellow Sea.

The Common Seal is not confined to salt water. There is a large colony inhabiting the freshwater Seal Lakes and Harrison Lake in northern Quebec. The Seal Lakes are ninety miles inland from the Hudson Bay but contain at least 1,000 Common Seals, cut off from the main herds in the Hudson Bay during the last 3,000 to 8,000 years.

Large breeding colonies are found along the Dutch, Frisian and Danish coasts. In Britain the breeding colonies are mainly centred upon the Wash (2,000 seals), the East Anglian coast, Shetland (over 400 seals), Orkney, the Inner and Outer Hebrides, the east and west coasts of Scotland, and Northern Ireland (350 seals). But outside the breeding season they are more generally distributed around the coasts.

Appearance and description

In colour both sexes are normally dark grey above, lighter below, and marked all over with black spots. North American males tend to be darker in colour than the females, though pure white specimens have been reported. The head is rounded, with a snub, up-turned nose bearing a pair of elongated nostrils arranged in the shape of a 'V', the lower ends of the nostrils almost touching.

Males grow as long as 6 feet and weigh as much as 550 pounds. The females are foot or so shorter, and less than half the weight.

Habitat and general habits

The Common Seal lives mainly along the coast and hauls out on land at every opportunity, usually at the edges of harbours, bays and estuaries, and on to sand-flats and mudbanks. Towards the northern parts of the species' range (in Shetland, for example, where L. S. V. and U. M. Venables made a detailed study) the seals will haul out on to rocky shores, and further north still on to the ice. The number of individuals that haul out appears to depend to a great extent on the state of the tide, the air temperature, and the turbulence of the water. Most of the seals haul out at night after feeding, but in Shetland they haul out at low tide irrespective of the time of day. When the seals are hauled out, an old male is generally on the lookout at the highest point to give warning of approaching danger. The species is quick to react to danger, especially to the human kind, and it is said that the Common Seal is able to distinguish between a boat with men on deck and a boat with the crew below or unmanned.

Close studies of the Common Seal colonies in Shetland and Faroe show that they usually prefer shallow bays with gradual slopes up to the land to facilitate hauling out. Many of the bays are only about 2 fathoms deep and thick with seaweed, and are popular because they are places where the pups can learn to fend for themselves. The seals of Shetland and the West Highlands, where they live far up the sea-lochs, will haul out on to shingle beaches and beaches with small rocks which are within the tides, avoiding those with large boulders. Many seals return and haul out at the same spot time after time, and some even bask on the same rock. Grey Seals inhabit the same regions but as they prefer more open coastlines there is little contact between the two species, though a

Common Seal was once seen chasing off a Grey Seal which attempted to haul out nearby.

On land the Common Seal moves with a caterpillar motion, its hind flippers pressed together. It is also able to raise itself almost vertical by resting on the hind part of the body.

In the water the Common Seal swims using its hind flippers, sculling with each flipper separately and alternately. In this way it is capable of speed of up to 15 miles per hour in short bursts, sometimes moving through the water with porpoise-like leaps. It does not usually dive suddenly but gradually submerges into the water like a submarine — and it *can* remain submerged for at least forty-five minutes.

Whilst in the water searching for food Common Seals are usually solitary; they take a wide variety of foods, practically anything that is available, including dab, plaice, flounder, goby, whiting, molluscs, crustaceans and, on occasion in the north of Scotland, even eiders and shelducks — though birds often share the same ground, provided the seals are harmlessly basking. They appear to be unable to sleep in the water but must haul out to do so, unlike the eared seals (such as *Callorhinus* and *Zalophus*) which are content to float on their backs in the water and doze. To this extent the Common Seal is still more tied to the land than the eared seals.

The Common Seal utters a variety of sounds depending on its age, the time of the year, habitat, and circumstances at the time. In general the pups emit a mewing cry, and the adults a barking growl. Other sounds include a loud snort audible for over a mile; a throaty grunt during the breeding season; a dog-like bark from aquarium specimens; and a short appealing hoot from a young pup separated from its mother.

The adult males pass through a period of fighting following the breeding season and the moult. The battles usually occur during October and November when the combatants charge into the water and grapple with each other, often inflicting deep wounds in the pelts. There is no explanation for this fighting, especially as it occurs *after* the breeding season.

The species has few natural enemies. Man is, of course, the greatest threat, but Common Seals in the North Atlantic are also preyed upon by Killer Whales, and those of the North Pacific by sharks. An 800 pound Great White Shark was found with a whole Common Seal pup in its stomach.

Seasonal movements

The Common Seal does not migrate. It will go on feeding trips, but these have nothing to do with the changing seasons.

Reproduction

Breeding occurs between May and October. The time of the pupping season and subsequent mating differs a little from region to region. In the Wash the pups are born during the first two weeks of June, whereas in Shetland and along the Dutch coast pupping occurs from mid-June until the beginning of July. On the Pacific side of the United States the pups are born earlier, beginning in May in the south and late May and early June in the north.

In Shetland during May the adults and sub-adults play in pairs, one male and one female. The pairs roll and twist in the water snarling and snapping at each other. This play is thought to be equivalent to courting, as copulation appears to occur afterwards, the cow rolling on her back with the male on top gripping her with his fore flippers. Following this *apparent* copulation the pair starts its rolling and twisting game again. This play-mating behaviour occurs throughout their range and is not peculiar to Shetland seals. In the Shetland group the play stops in mid-June with the onset of the pupping season.

The seals start to congregate in sheltered shallow bays, where the pregnant cows give birth to their pups in the water, although a few females haul out on offshore rocks or rocky beaches. The placentae and membranes are scattered over the whole pupping area but scavenging birds like Fulmars quickly clear them away. They mate about a month after the birth of the pups, copulating in the water after a period of rolling, twisting play.

Birth to maturity

At birth the pup is 2 to $2\frac{1}{2}$ feet in length, weighs up to 25 pounds, and is covered in a light grey woolly coat (the long silvery foetal coat was lost before birth). The newly-born seal is very weak, and floats vertically at the surface of the water with just its head and shoulders visible. The pup is suckled for three or four weeks, usually taking milk from the cow underwater, with the mother floating vertically. The pup stays under the water suckling for periods of up to six minutes.

During the first couple of days the pup is able to swim and dive, but its hind quarters are very weak and not until it is about three weeks old is it able to move its hind end like an adult. During the first few days the mother rarely leaves her pup; she steers it away from the deeper water with her fore flippers and may even take it on land on top of her shoulders. Once the pup is able to haul itself out on land the cow can suckle it there. At three weeks the pups have put on weight and are able to swim in the shallows and haul out without difficulty and with no assistance from the adult cows. Shortly after this time lactation ceases and the pups become independent. The adults start their moult after mating.

Sexual maturity is attained at 3 years of age.

The life expectation of the seals in the wild is not known, but specimens kept in captivity have lived to be over 12 years of age, and one at San Diego Zoo was over 17.

The species in relation to man

In Shetland the seals have suffered at the hands of man since the Iron and Bronze Ages. Archaeologists have found the bones of the Common Seal in excavated kitchen middens of these eras. The Vikings hunted the species in the ninth and tenth centuries.

Today, in the northern parts of its range, Eskimos hunt the Common Seal mainly for its pelt — especially the whitish, fine, close pelt of a pup under 6 weeks old, which fetches a better price. Until quite recently the Eskimos hunted the seal for food, and used the skins to make rawhide shoes (or rivlins) and pouches.

THE GREY SEAL (Plates 12 and 13) *Halichoerus grypus*

Distribution and estimated population

The Grey Seal is the largest surviving carnivore in the British Isles. It is also the most controversial — the centre, from time to time, of passionate arguments.

On the one hand it is damned as a criminal creature, the slayer of salmon and the ruination of the fisherman's livelihood. On the other hand it is defended with a degree of emotion peculiar to the British people — especially since the Government has permitted the selective killing (or culling) of the species, a decision which has been discussed earlier in this book.

The Grey Seal is common round the coasts of Britain, especially along the rocky western shores. In the west the largest breeding colonies are found on North Rona, Orkney, Shetland, the Hebrides, the Isle of Man, the island of Ramsey and the mainland Welsh coast, North Devon, Cornwall, the Scillies, and the Irish coasts. In the east the largest colony is on the Farne Islands. The range of the Grey Seal spreads outwards from Britain, from the Scottish islands to Iceland, and northeastwards to the coast of Norway as far as the mouth of the White Sea. The species is only rarely seen off the coasts of Holland, France and Germany.

The Grey Seal is not, however, confined only to this East Atlantic area; there are two other distinct populations, one in the West Atlantic and another in the Baltic Sea. In the West Atlantic the species is found in the Gulf of St Lawrence, around the coasts of Newfoundland, Nova Scotia and many of the islands in the Gulf; the largest breeding colony is in the Northumberland Strait. In the Baltic the largest breeding colonies are in the Gulf of Bothnia.

The world population was estimated by E. A. Smith in 1966 at 52,500 split up as follows:

Baltic 5,000
Norway 2,000
North East Europe   300
Faroe/Iceland 4,000
Great Britain 34,200
Ireland 2,000
North West Atlantic 5,000

Thus over 60 per cent of the Grey Seals of the world inhabit the shores of Britain, the vast majority off Scotland.

The West Atlantic Grey Seals became geographically isolated from those in the East about 100,000 years ago. The western population is thought to have separated into East Atlantic and Baltic groups some 9,000 years ago.

Appearance and description

Adult bull Grey Seals grow to over 9 feet in length and attain weights of up to 630 pounds. The cows are smaller, growing up to 7 feet in length and weighing up to 550 pounds. Members of the species vary greatly in colour, from dark to light grey, brown and silver. These variations in coat colour occur more amongst the bulls than the cows. The upper surface of the body is generally darker than the underparts, and the whole surface of the body is spotted to a varying degree. These spots are a useful guide to the sexes: males have light spots on a darker background; females have dark spots on a lighter background. Males can be further distinguished by their well-developed hump of a 'Roman nose', although sometimes a very old cow looks much the same. Many of the seals, especially those of Europe, have abnormally developed ear flaps, unlike any other Phocid.

Habitat and general habits

The only periods when Grey Seals can be studied properly are when they are on land, moulting and breeding. For much of the rest of the time they are out at sea, so not a great deal is known about their habits.

In Britain the adult females haul out on land in January to moult; they return to the sea in March and then the males haul out for their moult. The British seals prefer rocky coastlines and islands; the Baltic and West Atlantic seals choose mudbanks or sandbanks.

After they have moulted, the seals return to the sea to feed. It is hard to know exactly what the Grey Seal eats because it digests its food so rapidly that even a specimen caught shortly after a meal has an empty stomach or contents too well digested to recognise. The indications are, however, that the Grey Seal will eat almost anything that is available including fish, crustaceans and molluscs. Economically important fish such as salmon, herring, pollack, halibut, flat fish and flounder have been identified along with many others of little or no commercial value. The search for food takes the seals down to great depths, and off the Norwegian coast young seals have been caught as far down as 500 feet.

As with most seals, parasitic infestations are common not only in the digestive tract but in the pelt — 'Green Grey Seals' have been seen in Canada, for example, and it seems that the green colour is caused by algae growing over the seals' backs. (The same thing happens to Monk Seals.)

On land the Grey Seal is one of the most ungainly creatures, moving forward with a looping, caterpillar-like action, using its chest, fore flippers and hindquarters. The seals of Ramsey off the Pembrokeshire coast, on the other hand, progress over land on their sides rather than by the normal method of flopping along on the stomach.

In the water the Grey Seal displays a true mastery of its aquatic environment; it is equally at home streaking through the water face down, or on its back, or hovering vertically in one spot. It closes its nostrils and ear holes when it dives and in shallow water it can sometimes be seen sleeping at the bottom; it rises to the surface for a fresh supply of air, apparently automatically, takes a breath and sinks back to the bottom like a submarine, without once waking up.

Seasonal movements

The Grey Seal does not migrate although there is a certain amount of dispersal from the rookeries at the end of the breeding season. The pups, too, wander widely when they leave the breeding grounds and do not return for two years.

Reproduction

In the Gulf of St Lawrence and in the Baltic the pups are born during February and March, close to the edges of the winter ice. The majority of the British colonies, however, pup during the autumn between September and November; the Farnes colony is a little later (up until the end of December), and the Welsh colonies a little earlier. East Atlantic Grey Seals in the Scottish islands tend to pup well inland; elsewhere the pups are born between the low and high tide marks.

Little information is available on the breeding habits of the Gulf of St Lawrence and Baltic seals, as their breeding places — ice floes and the precarious edges of the solid ice — are practically inaccessible to man. The British colonies are not all easy to study either, and the caves and small coves where the seals choose to breed must be approached from the seaward side; but zoologists have managed to learn quite a lot about the organisation of the rookeries and the behaviour of the inmates there.

Some weeks before the breeding season begins the adult males and pregnant females start to gather near the breeding sites. There appear to be a number of bulls who are accepted as superior by the remainder of the males, and this band of *elite* males eventually hauls out unmolested and occupies the best sites in the rookery, depending on the topography of the breeding beach. If the beach is small and enclosed, the favoured areas may be next to the water. But if there is access to a turf interior with peat wallows, as on some of the Scottish islands, then the bulls may prefer inland stations. In Pembrokeshire the bull stays in the sea and his territory may extend over an area of sea shore, or a number of bays. Shortly after the élite have taken up their positions, the 'lesser' males start to haul out and wage a pitched battle on the shore. A bull hauling out is usually challenged by one already on land. The challenger lowers his head, opens his mouth, and hisses quietly. The newcomer either retreats back into the water or accepts the challenge and fights. The combatants slash sideways at each other with open mouths and inflict wounds on the sides of the neck and shoulders. When the fight has been decided the loser retires to the sea; he does not attempt to land again but disappears and wanders in the sea for a year before trying his luck again. Battles over, the rookery settles down, the superior bulls guarding the best territories against all-comers, and the remaining bulls ranged around in the second-best places.

The cows will not mate with the bulls until about two weeks after the birth of the pups that were conceived in the previous year. In the intervening period the bulls try to mate but are fiercely repelled by the cows. The birth of the pups is very rapid indeed; it usually takes only about fifteen seconds, although one cow achieved a record time of one second. The cows sever the umbilical cord by lashing the hind part of the body from side to side; they ignore the placenta and membranes and leave them scattered all over the breeding places to be disposed of by the gulls and other scavenging birds.

The cow suckles her pup several times a day. After each feed she goes off to muddy wallows and shallow pools, or swims in the sea if it is within easy reach.

Eventually the seals mate, either in the water or on land. A dominant bull, who may mate with 6 or 7 cows, becomes so preoccupied with his females that often he forgets his preciously guarded territory and it is taken over by one of the lesser bulls.

The non-pregnant cows and virgin cows do not appear at the rookeries, and are believed to mate elsewhere. The blastocyst remains free in the uterus for about three months after copulation.

At some British colonies a second haul-out, akin to that of the breeding season, appears to take place in the spring. This phenomenon has been called a 'false rut'; no one knows what the seals do in the rookeries at this time but they have not actually been seen mating. Perhaps this false rut is a behavioural remnant of a former breeding season — this would bring the British seals in line with the breeding times of the Baltic and West Atlantic groups.

Birth to maturity

At birth the pup is about 2 feet 6 inches in length, weighs about 35 pounds, and is covered in long white wool. In some colonies, especially those in the British Isles and Gulf of St Lawrence, the pups have lost their milk teeth before they are born, and the permanent teeth gradually develop from the time of birth onwards. In the Baltic the milk teeth are still present at birth but are lost shortly afterwards.

The pups are suckled for two or three weeks, by which time they have gained up to 100 pounds in weight (including 60 pounds of blubber) and the loose rolls of skin of the newly born pup have filled out and given the youngster a very rotund appearance.

When they have been weaned, the pups moult. The moult lasts two or three weeks during which time the pups take no food but live on their accumulated blubber. The fur moults firstly on the muzzle and flippers, then on the head, and lastly on the back and the rest of the body. On Ramsey there appears to be a pre-natal moult and the pups consequently leave for the sea at an earlier time than elsewhere. Although the pups are able to swim at birth, most of them do not enter the water until after the moult.

As the pups can be handled comparatively easily, many have been tagged or otherwise marked in recent years, especially in Pembrokeshire, on the Farne Islands and at various Scottish rookeries. Recoveries of marked seals provide evidence of wide dispersal of pups, as mentioned on page 114. Those from

Pembrokeshire reach Brittany quite quickly, with an odd one as far as Spain; from north and east Britain they cross to Denmark and Norway, Faroe and Holland. Across the Atlantic a tagged pup from Nova Scotia has reached Newfoundland.

The cows are sexually mature at 3 years of age and may bear pups up to at least 35 years of age. The bulls are sexually mature at 6 or 7 years of age but probably not capable of holding territory until they are at least 10 years old. Most cows live much longer than bulls; a 35 year old cow is not uncommon, whereas few bulls are over 20 years, due to a high mortality rate during their reproductive life. The possible life span is 40 years or more for both sexes.

The species in relation to man

For many years Grey Seals have been hunted in all the areas they inhabit. In the Baltic this has caused a terrific reduction in their numbers; in the Danish regions of the Baltic, for example, only a small colony has survived, and it is thought that these seals are not breeding and so must die out during the next thirty years or so. In the Gulf of St. Lawrence local fishermen hunted the seals for their pelts and meat. They went for the pups mostly, especially the youngest pups which had not yet taken to the water, and they killed them by smashing their heads with large clubs. They killed adults occasionally too, using firearms.

Today the Grey Seal is officially protected in some areas. But there are still places where it is the victim of incessant assault by man. In the Gulf of Bothnia, for instance, it is hunted all the year round — over the ice in winter and from boats in summer. In Norway most of the seals are safe in a reserve near Trondheim but in the Faroes and Iceland they are completely unprotected and are shot indiscriminately by fishermen for 'sport'. At one time the hunters used the oil and blubber from the seals — now they do not even bother to recover the bodies.

I

9. Other Seals of the Northern Hemisphere

THE BEARDED SEAL (Plate 14)   *Erignathus barbatus*

Distribution and estimated population and allied forms

The Bearded Seal is found at the edge of the Arctic ice all around the North Pole. It frequents coastal waters, preferring those up to 25 fathoms deep, and sometimes individuals swim into bays and estuaries. They avoid those coasts where the ice is solid in winter. Mostly they haul out on to ice floes, but they are occasionally seen resting on stony beaches.

In the Western Pacific Bearded Seals are found as far south as Hokkaido, and in the Western Atlantic as far south as Nova Scotia. But on the eastern sides of these oceans they do not penetrate to such low latitudes. They are seen off Alaska but only rarely off Europe, although individuals have been reported from Britain and France. Some authorities recognise two sub-species — *Erignathus barbatus barbatus* and *E.b. nauticus*. Their ranges correspond roughly to those of the Atlantic and Pacific Walrus respectively. The skull of *E.b. barbatus* is said to be somewhat narrower and longer than that of *E.b. nauticus*, but whether the two forms are really distinct remains arguable.

The world population of the species is probably more than 100,000.

Early historical records

The first account of the species was given by Steller in 1751. He used the Kamchadal Eskimo name 'lach-tak', a name which still survives in native use today.

Appearance and description

The adult female Bearded Seal is about 7 feet 6 inches in length. Fully adult males have been reported with lengths ranging from 8 feet to 12 feet, but 10 feet is more common. Weighing perhaps 1000 pounds, they are the second largest true seal of the Northern Hemisphere, surpassed only by the Elephant Seal. There is no difference in the colour of the sexes but individuals vary quite considerably — grey or yellow-brown are the commonest shades. Along the top of the back there is a darker stripe, and there may be some spotting.

The face is given an endearing expression by the tufts of long bristly whiskers pointing downwards on either side of the muzzle; from them the species gets its English and scientific names. When the seal is wet the whiskers are long and pointed, but when the fur is dry they curl at the ends and give it a rather bedraggled appearance. Most other kinds of seals have whiskers which vary regularly in diameter all along their length, giving a beaded appearance, but the Bearded Seals, and also the Monk Seals, differ in that their whiskers are of constant diameter or taper smoothly without any beading.

Like the Monk Seals, the Bearded Seal is unusual in having four mammae. Most seals have only two.

Many people have commented on the poor condition of Bearded Seals' teeth. In many adults the teeth are worn right down or lost, and even in those with no dental deficiency the teeth are often loose enough to be pulled out with the fingers.

The middle digit of the forelimb is longer than the others in this seal, which gives a rectangular outline to the end of the fore flipper and has led to sealers calling it the 'square-flipper'. This unusual shaped fore flipper provides yet another point of difference between the Bearded Seal and other phocids. In spite of these peculiarities it has on more than one occasion been confused with the Grey Seal.

Habitat and general habits

The Bearded Seals are solitary animals and are never seen in large aggregations. By nature they are curious creatures and seem drawn to investigate any boat in the vicinity. Even the sound of a gun appears to attract rather than repel them, and this makes them an easy prey for the huntsmen. They show no fear of boats in the water, but if surprised by an intruder on land they seem paralysed by fright and are unable to stir themselves to escape. Any Polar Bear or Eskimo that comes upon a Bearded Seal resting on the ice may count upon an easily caught meal.

This seal has some strange behaviour traits. On occasions when it has been disturbed without being immobilised by fear, it has been seen to turn somersaults as it dives into the water to safety. And males have been seen fighting each other not with their teeth as other seals do but with their fore flippers — unlikely though it sounds.

The adults apparently communicate with the pups in the water (but not on land) by whistling.

The mode of life of the Bearded Seal is very like that of the Walrus. Both animals gather immobile or slow-moving invertebrate prey from the sea bed. The 'beard' of the seal is almost certainly used as a shovel and strainer for food which includes clams, shrimps, crabs, sea-cucumbers, octopuses, and sometimes slow fish such as sculpin and flounder. Some of this food is brought up from considerable depths — *Erignathus* is an accomplished diver if not a fast swimmer.

Seasonal movements

The Bearded Seal does not really migrate but as it lives among ice floes (avoiding fast ice) it tends to drift north on the floes in the spring and south again in the winter.

Reproduction

Bearded Seals do not congregate in one spot to breed but the families may haul out near one another so that groups of up to 50 seals may be seen in certain areas. The time of the pups' births varies according to latitude and whereas south of Kamchatka pups may be seen in February, pupping occurs later in the north so that most are born during April and May. Mating takes place within a few weeks after the cows have given birth to the pups, but the recently pupped females do not conceive. In the case of cows that have not borne pups that year the blastocyst implants ten weeks after mating, and the gestation period is about eleven months. The breeding cycle is thus an unusual one. The female produces one pup *every other year only* — apparently because after pupping the cow does not ovulate again until after the breeding season is over.

The female Bearded Seal is ready to breed at 6 years of age, the male at 7 years.

Birth to maturity

The pups are usually born on ice floes and at birth are 4 feet long and weigh about 80 pounds. The pup is covered in a soft wool of a dark grey colour which moults after a fortnight to a short grey coat like the adult's. Lactation probably finishes then, although the pup follows the cow around for a long time afterwards.

The species in relation to man

The Eskimos, who call the Bearded Seal 'Ogjuk', utilise practically every inch of the animal in one way or another. They consider the flesh a delicacy, especially if it is allowed to mature for a while after killing; they use the skin for clothing, and in Alaska they consider the best leather for the soles of their boots comes from the Bearded Seal; they manufacture dog harnesses, fishing lines and boats out of it (15 seals provide the skin for one boat or *oomiak*) and use the fat from the blubber.

A certain number of Bearded Seals are taken by sealers in the north Atlantic but since they cannot be found in large concentrations it is not profitable to mount expeditions to hunt them exclusively.

THE RINGED SEAL (Plate 15)   *Pusa hispida*

Distribution, allied forms and estimated population

The Ringed Seals live all around the North Polar regions — from the ice and waters of the sub-Arctic right up to the North Pole itself. A number of them also inhabit inland freshwater lakes in northwestern Europe, notably Saimaa in Finland, which is over 200 feet above sea-level, and Ladoga in Russia. It is an abundant and thriving species and it has been estimated that there are

I*

certainly not less than two and a half million of them in the world and possibly as many as six million.

Individual Ringed Seals from different geographical areas quite constantly show distinctive colorations and cranial characteristics. Experts are able to separate the varieties with a fair degree of certainty, and the species has been divided into several sub-species. But scientific authors have yet to decide precisely how many there are. Ognev in his book *Mammals of the U.S.S.R.* names seven sub-species:

Pusa hispida pomororum in the White and Barents Seas.

P.h. hispida around Greenland and Spitzbergen.

P.h. botnica in the Baltic Sea.

P.h. saimensis in Lake Saimaa.

P.h. ladogensis in Lake Ladoga.

P.h. birulai along the north coast of Siberia.

and *P.h. ochotensis* in the Sea of Okhotsk.

Scheffer, in his book *Seals, Sealions, and Walruses* names only five of those above — *hispida, ochotensis, botnica, ladogensis* and *saimensis*. But he adds one other, *P.h. krascheninikovi*, found in the north of the Bering Sea and around the Kurile Islands and Hokkaido.

Raymond Hall and Kelson in their book *The Mammals of North America* add two further names to the lengthy list — *P.h. beaufortiana* inhabiting the seas from Alaska eastwards to Mackenzie and Coronation Gulf; and *P.h. soperi* inhabiting the east side of Foxe Basin and Nettilling Lake on Baffin Island.

Appearance and description

Ringed Seals from different areas vary considerably in colour, ranging from light yellow through olive to black. However, they all have the characteristic light ringed spots which have given this seal its common name. The two main colour varieties are the very dark and the light. The former have an almost black back with a dark grey undersurface; the latter have a slate grey back marked with rings, and a uniformly grey undersurface without markings.

The Ringed Seal is one of the smaller seals; the males may grow to 5 feet 6 inches in length, though many adults never exceed 4 feet 6 inches; the maximum weight is in the region of 250 pounds. There is little difference in size between the sexes, but the males are perhaps on average an inch or so longer. There have been reports that a dwarf variety exists alongside the normal type in the waters from Novaya Zemlya to Svalbard (Spitzbergen). But there is some doubt and speculation as to whether these reports are reliable.

It is possible to estimate the age of a Ringed Seal by examining its teeth and claws. During March, April and May the deposition of dentine, the hard tissue that forms the main part of teeth, is less dense than in the following two months. This leads to a ringed appearance in the teeth which provides a reasonably accurate indication of age and has led to the discovery of one old male of 40 years of age — the most senior Ringed Seal known. The claws, too, have bands which give a clue to the age of an individual seal provided it is under 10 years old.

Scientists have observed that those seals born on ice which is stable until late in the season are larger than those born on the peripheral ice; they have also found that the most suitable areas for pupping are occupied by the older seals.

Habitat and general habits

The species takes a wide variety of foods which are available in both the inshore and offshore waters. The diet consists of fish such as polar cod, and crustaceans such as *Mysis* which are abundant near the shores. Further out from the shoreline planktonic crustaceans such as *Themisto* are more abundant. Although this planktonic food is plentiful in deeper waters the seals may dive for fish and crustaceans to depths of up to 300 feet. The range of the species is apparently not limited by the food supply as there is suitable food well outside the delineated range — in some parts of the Hudson Bay, for example, where the seals are not known.

During the breeding season and the moult which follows shortly afterwards the seals do not take any food; their fast lasts from April until late June or July.

Seasonal movements

Ringed Seals do not migrate. They may disperse from the breeding and moulting areas but generally they remain within the limits of the fast ice throughout the year, rarely straying more than 10 miles out to sea or at the very most 80 miles.

Reproduction

The majority of the pups are born during the first two weeks of April, though the breeding season may last till mid-May. The pups are born on the ice in deep bays close to the shore. The pregnant cows dig out dens in the snow that covers the ice, making sure that the entrances to the dens are near to the water. The den in which the pup is born is low and spindle-shaped and may be over 10 feet long; the heat of the animal's body melts the snow which then freezes into ice so that the roof of the den becomes very strong.

During the breeding season the males literally stink. It is a very strong and very unpleasant odour and it may have a sexual significance — certainly the young, sexually immature males do not smell in this way. The non-pregnant cows are the first to be mated; the cows that were pregnant are mated two weeks after they have given birth, while they are still suckling their pups. It is not until three and a half months after copulation that the blastocyst implants in the uterus.

Birth to maturity

At birth the pup is about 2 feet long, weighs up to 10 pounds, and is covered in a white woolly coat which is moulted at two to three weeks.

The adult cow feeds the pup for up to three months, by which time the youngster has started to take solid food. The long period of lactation may be attributed to the fact that the species breeds on solid ice, unlike some species which breed on floes, and since there is little danger of the ice disintegrating or melting, time is not a factor of great importance.

The females attain sexual maturity at between 5 and 8 years of age, the majority of them between 6 and 7. The males begin to stink at around the same age.

The species in relation to man

The Ringed Seal has always been hunted by Eskimos for food, clothing, and fuel, and it is still the mainstay of some Eskimos' economy.

The species in captivity

The species has been kept in a number of the world's zoos, including Hagenbeck's Tierpark at Stellingen, the London Zoo (as early as 1905) and the New York Aquarium, which received its first specimen, captured in the Bering Sea, in 1961. Stockholm Zoo kept a female Ringed Seal from 1914 until 1929, the record length of time in captivity for this species to date. On New Year's Day 1929 this cow gave birth to a stillborn pup, the father of which, surprisingly, was a Grey Seal.

THE CASPIAN SEAL   *Pusa caspica*

Distribution and estimated population

As the name suggests, the Caspian Seal is found throughout the Caspian Sea, although during the summer months the majority remain on the sandy bars and desert islands in the south, where the sea is much deeper and cooler. In the winter they move to the north of the Caspian, where ice forms over the shallower waters.

The present population of the species is probably well over one million.

Early historical records

The Caspian Seal was first described by Gmelin in 1770, and he simply called it *Der Seehund*. Since that time the species has had at least ten different scientific names, both specific and sub-specific, including — *Der Caspische Seehund*, Schreber 1776; *Phoca vitulina*, Erxleben 1777; *Phoca vitulina caspica*, Gmelin 1788; *Phoca caspica*, Nilsson 1837; *Callocephalus caspicus*, Gray 1844; *Phoca canina*, Pallas 1831; *Phoca foetida caspica*, Nordquist 1899; and *Phoca hispida caspica*, Trouesant 1904. It was given its present name, *Phoca (Pusa) caspica* by Allen in 1880.

Appearance and description

The adult male Caspian Seal is 4 feet 6 inches to 4 feet 10 inches long, the female about 3 inches shorter. Their body weight reaches a maximum of just under 200 pounds.

There is little colour difference between the sexes; both adult males and females bear glossy fur which is olive-grey with darker spots. Younger animals under 2 years of age are darker and less marked. During the second year the coat colour lightens and the markings are much more distinct.

Although the sexes are similar in colour and markings, they can be distinguished from one another — the male has a thicker head, a longer muzzle, and a longer neck than the female.

Habitat and general habits

During the summer months, after the pups have been born and weaned and the adults have passed through their moult, most of the seals inhabit the southern half of the Caspian Sea. They haul out on shallow sloping shores of the sandbanks, islands and mainland, and jostle with each other for the favourite positions — which are right next to the water's edge. The seal's sense of smell is thought to be very well developed and all the animals lie with their heads upwind so that at the first sight or scent of danger they bustle to the water and swim far out to sea. On land the seal is very awkward and it moves about only when absolutely necessary by contorting the body and hopping along using its fore flippers and pelvis. Although clumsy, it is capable of a fair turn of speed when frightened and is almost able to keep pace with a running man. But the seals are, of course, primarily adapted for moving in water, and they are rapid and graceful swimmers. Their speed is useful for catching fish but they do not always race through the water; they can often be seen resting motionless at the surface, moving around only with the motion of the waves. They are equally at ease under the water, and may dive to great depths, remaining submerged for as long as twenty minutes.

In the north of the Caspian, where the seals spend the winter, the ice starts to form as a smooth field due to the comparative freshness of the water, which is only half as 'salty' as that of the great oceans, the absence of currents, and the lack of snow storms; if a wind blows up, then the ice starts to break up and is thrown into jagged mounds. The depth of the Caspian increases from north to south and the limit of the ice is about half way between the two ends.

During the winter the seals spend a great deal of the time under the ice, which means they must construct exit and breathing holes. The exit holes may be up to 2 feet across; the breathing holes — small apertures in ice domes 6 inches high and 2½ feet wide — are only 2 inches in diameter and under them the seals can be heard snorting and puffing. Both types of hole are usually made early in the season and are maintained as the ice gets thicker; the seals are thus saved the arduous task of working through thick, fully formed ice.

Under the ice the seals feed on fish, molluscs, and crustaceans, including in their diet sculpin, beach fleas, and silversides. They rarely take commercially valuable fish although some seals, famished after the moult in the spring, have been known to take herring from fishermen's nets. Cases have been recorded of seals gorging themselves to death on sculpin.

When the ice disintegrates in the spring the carcasses of those animals which have died under the ice (probably through suffocation) can be seen floating at the surface of the water, and are known locally as 'floaters'.

Seasonal movements

During the autumn the females start to move north, followed a little later by the males. The journey is rarely broken; few seals haul out during the course of the migration and the majority of them arrive in the north before the ice has started to form and haul out on land in huge colonies. At this time the seals are well fed, and while they are on land they are the prime target of hunters.

In the summer, after breeding and moulting, the seals start the general move to the south.

Reproduction

Although the whole of the northern Caspian Sea freezes over, the rookeries are concentrated in the north-eastern sector, where the ice generally forms earlier than elsewhere. As soon as the ice has formed and has started to break up into floes, the females choose the more suitable floes and start to construct exit and breathing holes long before the birth of the pups.

The pups are born during January and the beginning of February well away from the edges of the floes. The pregnant females tend to form rookeries together according to their age and stage of pregnancy, and the large area in which the pups are born is divided up into numerous rookeries of several hundred seals each.

After the birth of the pups the males start to seek out the cows, and ferocious fighting amongst the bulls is common. Savage wounds are often inflicted with the teeth, and the pelts of the combatants are often torn to shreds. Mating between the victors of the battles and the cows takes place during late February and early March in the water, although there is evidence that some mate on the ice. There follows a gestation period of eleven months.

Birth to maturity

The newborn pups are small, may weigh only 6 pounds, and are covered in a soft yellowish coat which turns pure white within two or three days. The cow is extremely attached to her offspring and when she feeds it she nurses it with her fore flippers; if she is frightened off the ice by hunters she will immediately head for the nearest breathing or exit hole in the ice and peer through at the hunters and particularly at the pup. When the pup catches sight of its mother it lets out what has been described as 'a rather human wail'— as well it might, because the hunters have been waiting for the moment when the mother appeared at the hole to strike. Often if danger threatens while the mother and pup are together, the cow will carry the pup to the nearest exit hole in the ice, wait until the pup has obtained a firm grip with its teeth on her fur, and then dive into the water, dragging the pup along behind (the very young pup does not enter the water voluntarily until it has stopped being suckled). Apart from the sealers, the cows must keep alert for eagles, including Golden Eagles, which will carry off the pup unless the adult is close enough to her offspring to defend it.

Two weeks after birth and while still being suckled, the pup passes through its first moult, at which time it weighs between 10 and 20 pounds. During the moult it loses its woolly white coat and assumes a pelt of short, coarse, grey fur; the pups often take to the water at this time and are capable of making their own way to safety via the exit holes. By the end of February the moult is completed and the cows have deserted the pups; then the 'greylings' leave the floes, take to the water and form new herds. Pups which have been abandoned or have lost their mothers sometimes survive through the moulting period on the blubber they accumulated when the parent was present. But the abandoned pup is nonetheless starving; it cries day and night, and tries to abate its hunger by licking and sucking the ice. If it survives until its moult is complete then it may make its way to the water and start to take solid food.

During very severe winters the exit holes may ice over before the greylings are ready to depart. When this happens the pups may have to cross miles of open ice in search of the open water. In 1924 there was a very hard and cold winter and a sealing vessel was trapped in the ice but was able to amass a considerable haul simply by capturing greylings which were passing the ship on their way to water. Many of these pups had worn away the fur on their undersides during their passage over the ice.

The species in relation to man

The annual catch is at present between 100,000 and 115,000. Between the end of January and the beginning of March the pups are killed on the floes. Later the hunters concentrate on the older animals passing through their moult along the edges of the melting ice. Hunting with seine nets is also undertaken between mid-November and December in the open waters during the seal migrations.

THE BAIKAL SEAL (Plate 15)   *Pusa sibirica*

Distribution and estimated population

The Baikal Seal is the only seal which lives entirely in fresh water. It derives it common name from Lake Baikal, which is situated in Siberia near the Mongolian border, over 1,500 miles inland from the Laptev Sea to the north. Baikal is the deepest lake in the world (over 5,000 feet deep in parts) and is some 400 miles long. The seals are found throughout the lake, although the majority inhabit its northern waters. No one is sure exactly how many of them live there but estimates range from 40,000 to 100,000.

Appearance and description

The Baikal Seal is small; neither sex grows longer than 4 feet 6 inches. The weight of the carcass is most often about 150 pounds, but after the period of heavy feeding and before the fast it can be considerably more, especially the female's. There is a record of a female that had a blubber weight of 200 pounds alone.

In colour the sexes are similar — olive-brown to brownish-grey on the back, with lighter yellowish flanks and underparts.

Habitat and general habits

Very little is known of the summer activities of these seals as they spend the warmer months in inaccessible and little frequented localities. They are occasionally seen in large herds on off-shore rocks, basking in the sun. They are extremely cautious animals and approach the rocks from the water with considerable trepidation, but once they have hauled out and settled down to basking a man can approach without disturbing them. Those of the herd which are awake and alert raise themselves up with craning necks and when they sight danger plunge into the water.

The seals' diet appears to consist entirely of fish, and mainly of two species which are found only in Lake Baikal — *Comephorus baicalensis* and *Cottocomephorus gewinki*. Although other commercially more important fishes such as omuls and grayling live in the lake, the seals do not eat these, and as a consequence the local fishing industry does not suffer any damage.

In November, when winter is under way, the seals gather together in large numbers in Chivyrkui Bay, at the northern end of the lake. The waters of Baikal are very turbulent and the winter ice does not form a complete and unbroken cover over the entire surface until late December. But in Chivyrkui Bay the ice forms earlier, in November, and the seals favour it for this reason — though sometimes the swell will break up the early ice and groups of seals may find themselves floating out into the open water on broken floes. Once the whole surface of the lake is frozen solid, however, the seals remain in the water under the ice where the temperature is much warmer than that of the air above. (The water temperature may be just below zero Centigrade, whereas that of the air may be as low as −45 degrees Centigrade.) During this part of the winter the seals maintain breathing holes through the ice, and it is near these holes that the pregnant females construct the dens in which, later in the year, they will give birth to their young. To make a den the cow simply burrows into the snow piled on the ice and gradually the heat of her body thaws the snow and enlarges the cavity to the required size — sometimes up to 3 feet in diameter, with room for two pups.

By the end of the winter as the ice starts to break up, the males and those females that are not pregnant come out into the patches of open water, or break out through their breathing holes.

Reproduction

The pups are born in the dens towards the middle of March after a gestation period of nine months. It is still the depths of Siberian winter when they are born and the dens — frozen so solid that they will bear a man's weight — are completely invisible from the outside. By the beginning of June, when the ice has split up into many small floes, the seals will mate again. Generally they copulate in the water.

Birth to maturity

At birth the pups average 2 feet in length and weigh only 8 pounds. Their pelt consists of long, white woolly fur.

The pups take their mothers' milk until as late as mid-May when the mothers start to mate again, but usually they will have been weaned on to solid food before then — small sculpin (a kind of fish) have been found in the dens and are probably brought back by the mothers to feed the young.

The pups spend the crucial stages of their infancy — birth, lactation, moulting and weaning — entirely inside their dens in the snow, and the heat and movements of their bodies serve to enlarge their accommodation to as much as 6 feet across. But by early summer the sun starts to thaw the walls of the dens, and the young seals emerge into the daylight and lie basking on the ice or make occasional sallies into the water. Not until the ice cover on the lake has completely disappeared do the pups take to the water and visit the rocks and shores like the adults. Four more years must pass, though, before they reach sexual maturity and full adulthood.

The species in relation to man

The seals are hunted mainly by the Buryat people on the western and eastern shores — chiefly in spring, when the animals are either shot on the ice or trapped in nets in the water. The hunters — camouflaged in white clothing and white headgear, with tinted spectacles to shield their eyes from the glare of the snow — approach the seals on sail sleds. As soon as a hunter spots the black shape of a seal in the distance he hoists the sail, which hides him from view, and pushes the sled to within 50 yards of the animal — a range at which he can hardly miss.

In the south of the lake some seals are caught in the spring with horsehair seine nets. These large mesh nets are weighted and lowered into the water from long poles, then pushed under the ice near to the breathing holes. Mostly young seals are captured in this way, but it is not a very profitable occupation as the pelts are of poor quality and there is little blubber.

Recent figures on the annual kill are not available but, in 1925, 9,000 seals were being taken each year by some 550 sealers.

THE HARP SEAL (Plate 15)   *Pagophilus groenlandicus*

Distribution and estimated population

Pagophilus, which means ice-lover (from the Greek *pagos*, 'ice', and *philos*, 'loving'), inhabits the northern Atlantic Ocean and Arctic Ocean. The species ranges from Northern Russia across the Arctic and North Atlantic through Spitzbergen and Jan Mayen to Greenland, then southwards to Newfoundland, and northwards and eastwards into Baffin Bay and through the Hudson Strait into Hudson Bay. Harp Seals rarely visit Iceland, but appear to be present in the sea or on the ice all around Greenland with the exception of the northern coast. It has been named ice-lover, but the majority of Harp Seals spend the greater part of the year in the open water and out at sea.

Although most of the seals remain in the Arctic and far northern Atlantic, a few specimens have been reported from the shores of Britain — off Scotland and the Hebrides, and in the Bristol Channel and the River Teign in Devon.

The world population of the species is probably more than five million, divided into three fairly distinct groups, each with its own breeding area — one in the White Sea (one million), another in the Greenland Sea north of Jan Mayen (750,000) and the third round Newfoundland, in the Gulf of St Lawrence and on the east coast of Labrador (three million). By tagging individual seals from each of these areas and watching their movements scientists have learnt that members of one population do not interchange with those of another. Although there do appear to be three distinct breeding populations, and in 1937 Smirnov gave the three populations the status of 'sub-species' (he actually named only two of these), there are no morphological differences between the 'sub-species'. Scientists have therefore not generally accepted them.

Early historical records

The species was first named *Phoca groenlandica* by Fabricius in 1776, but he apparently did not give a description of the animal he was naming. A year later Erxleben provided the necessary description and the name *Phoca groenlandica* is usually attributed to him. In 1850 the present generic name *Pagophilus* was introduced by Gray.

Appearance and description

There is little difference in size between the males and the females, both sexes attaining lengths of up to 6 feet and weights of around 400 pounds. In colour the male is greyish-white with a black muzzle and black markings around the tail. The seal is sometimes called the 'Saddleback', as there is a distinct U-shaped black marking along each of the flanks joining on top of the back. The females and some of the males do not bear such distinct markings and they may be absent altogether or replaced by black spots. There appears to be yet another variation in which the body is spotted all over in black.

Habitat and general habits

The Harp Seal is a gregarious animal and only very old males tend to live alone or in small groups. The Russians have a name for these old animals — *odinets* or *odinetsy*, which mean 'hermits'. The seal spends most of the year at sea, where it is an extremely agile and powerful swimmer and feeds on crustaceans, and fish such as polar cod (northern haddock) and herring. When it hauls out on land or ice to breed or moult it is very ungainly and slow and feeds very little or not at all. The moulting rookeries are even larger than the breeding colonies and may number tens of thousands of seals.

The very young pups utter cries which have been compared to a miaowing cat, whilst the yearlings squeal with a sad, doleful note, and the adults bark like hoarse dogs.

Seasonal movements

Seasonal movements do occur, the general movement being north in the summer after moulting, and south during the winter to the breeding grounds.

In the winter those animals which have been feeding in the waters between Greenland and Baffin Island, and those in Hudson Bay, move southwards to the Gulf of St Lawrence, where they gather in the rookeries. After the breeding season they move northwards to the moulting grounds, and at the completion of the moult start the general summer movement towards the north. The Jan Mayen colony carries out similar movements although they may occur a month later than those of the St Lawrence group; after the breeding season the seals move to the ice north of the island, then after the moult continue northwards and eastwards to Greenland and Spitzbergen in the late spring. The White Sea population undergoes similar movements and arrives in the White Sea from the winter feeding grounds to the east and north (mainly the seas around Spitzbergen) during the early spring for the breeding season. During the first 50 years of this century the temperature of the water in the White Sea has risen and the ice, and therefore the rookeries, have gradually receded to the south away from the open sea.

Reproduction

The breeding season of the Harp Seal throughout its range is between January and April, and most of the pups are born between the end of February and the beginning of March (a little later in the Jan Mayen population).

At the beginning of the breeding season the animals haul out in large numbers on to heavy pack ice or floating ice floes. During this period of life on the ice the seals need a way of getting to and from the water but instead of making breathing holes they rely on the water 'leads' between the floes; it is among these that they surface to breathe after swimming in the water under the ice. Often, however, they have to use exit holes in the ice because the pupping places, to afford greater protection for the young, are well away from the ice edge. These exit holes are not constructed by the seals through thick, well-formed ice but are natural openings which have been kept open by the seals as the ice thickens all around. An exit hole may be maintained in this way through ice which is 3 feet thick. The hole is 2 or 3 feet across at the top, widening towards the base of the ice; usually it is surrounded by a small mound of ice. If for any reason a seal's exit hole becomes unusable it will share the exit of another seal, and several seals may end up sharing one hole.

The pups are believed to be born at night or early in the morning. The pregnant cows lie on the ice and the pups are born 6 or 7 feet from one another. The cow rarely leaves her pup during the first week. After this she may leave it for short periods, plopping into the water while the disconsolate pup crawls bleating around the ice. The females often patrol the water, guarding the pups and visiting them at intervals to suckle. If they are disturbed while in the water they do not rush to defend their offspring but disappear out to sea. If disturbed while on land with the pups, some of the cows defend their pups vigorously while others 'freeze' — as do the pups.

The males and females sometimes gather together in small family groups, but mostly the males keep to themselves in groups of a dozen or so.

Mating takes place a fortnight after the birth of the pups and after suckling has ceased, either in the water or on the ice. The males often fight amongst themselves using their teeth and flippers. The gestation period is 10 to 11 months though the blastocyst is not implanted until 11 weeks after copulation.

When the seals have finished mating, the rookeries start to break up and the males move off northwards to the moulting lairs where they congregate during March; a month later the females and pups join them.

Birth to maturity

At birth the pups are about 2 feet 6 inches long, weigh about 25 pounds, and are covered in a soft, curly, yellowish wool coat which turns pure white during the first three days. The newborn pup is very thin but it drinks heartily of its mother's milk (the mother lying on her side and stroking her pup with her fore flipper while she suckles) so that by the end of two weeks it has put on 2 inches of blubber and gained as much as 47 pounds in weight — in contrast to its mother who loses an average of 40 pounds of blubber during parturition and lactation. A lot of the pup's phenomenal growth is explained by the richness of the milk it feeds on, which is very thick and creamy and contains 42 per cent fat and 11 per cent protein.

During the lactation period the cows sometimes leave their pups and return to the water for short spells. While the cows are away the pups lie peacefully on the ice unless disturbed by intruders such as sealers, when they act in one of two ways — they either attempt to crawl away, or they 'freeze'. When 'freezing' they press their fore flippers to their sides, close their eyes, and draw their heads into the rolls of blubber around the neck. A man can handle and even pick up a youngster when it is in this pose, and it will not move — only very occasionally will a pup attempt to escape once it has been picked up. (This 'freezing' instinct when danger threatens is common amongst many animals.) Many youngsters are camouflaged, for the white coat of the young Harp Seal blends in with the background of ice and snow, but if the camouflage is to work efficiently the animal must keep fairly still, and when danger is in evidence then stillness is imperative. If this is unsuccessful there is always the last resort — flight or fight. If the mother happens to be present when the sealer approaches she may defend her pup or push it into the comparative safety of the water (the pups often take to the water naturally within two or three days of birth).

The pups have no natural enemies, man excepted, but dangers are inherent in their habitat. Waves can sweep them off the ice, and the continual breaking up of the ice can throw the youngsters into the sea or crush them.

The pups are weaned on to solid food in the form of floating crustaceans which are plentiful around the edges of the ice. Later they are able to take both the pelagic crustaceans and also those at the sea bottom, along with some fish.

When the pups stop being suckled they weigh approximately 70 pounds and pass through their first moult; at two weeks the wool begins to fall, exposing an underlying short, grey, stiff fur; at four weeks the moult is complete and the 'greylings' are all uniformly accoutred in fur coats half an inch thick. By the time the pup is a year old the coat has darkened under the body, and spot markings have appeared all over. By the second year the coat is a uniform grey colour, and by the third year the males have achieved the adult saddle marking, but are still not sexually mature. There has been some disagreement as to when Harp Seals achieve maturity, but it is now generally accepted that the males are sexually mature at 8 years of age; the females become mature at 6 and may bear pups until the age of 16 to 20. The average length of life of a Harp Seal is well over 20 years, and there is every reason to believe the upper limit is over 30 years.

The species in relation to man

Harp Seals have been hunted from Newfoundland for at least 200 years. The largest recorded haul was in 1831 when 687,000 seals were killed, but this total probably included a number of Hooded Seals.

The first recorded sealing expedition to Jan Mayen was in 1720, and by the early nineteenth century sealers were taking annual hauls of 200,000 seals. During this century the quota has dropped considerably and the annual haul has been between 20,000 and 40,000.

In the White Sea area, and around Novaya Zemlya and Spitzbergen in the open Arctic Sea large scale commercial hunting did not start until the last quarter of the nineteenth century. At this time catches of up to 10,000 per annum were common. Early in the 1900s the yearly kill had risen to 40,000. This total rose considerably until 1925 when 500,000 Harp Seals were slaughtered — the largest, and saddest, haul recorded there.

At the present time the annual world haul of the Harp Seals has been estimated at 500,000, of which about 200,000 are taken from the Newfoundland area, 100,000 from the White Sea region, and another 200,000 from the Jan Mayen and Greenland Sea areas.

The hunting season is relatively short, between the beginning of March and the beginning of May. About two-thirds of those seals killed are pups, either whitecoats or greylings. The coat of the greyling is probably the more valuable as it is thicker and warmer than that of the whitecoat. The pups are hunted and killed at the breeding rookeries during March, but the older animals are taken during the latter half of April and early May in the moulting lairs. The fur of the older animal is not as valuable as that of the pups, but the profits obtained on the oil from the older animals accounts for about 50 per cent of the total.

THE RIBBON SEAL (Plate 15)   *Histriophoca fasciata*

Distribution and estimated population

The Ribbon Seal — like its southern cousins, the Antarctic seals — is very little known. It lives in the northern Pacific between the great continents of Asia and North America, where it is confined to the western half of the Bering Sea, ranging northwards to the Arctic and southwards around Kamchatka into the Okhotsk Sea as far as Sakhalin Island.

Ribbon Seals normally inhabit open waters and ice floes, but occasionally they visit the shores of the mainland and islands. The species is rarely seen in large congregations but small herds have been seen on solid and floating ice in Aniwa Bay, the large bay between the twin promontories forming the southern tip of Sakhalin, whence they spread northwards along the coasts of the island at certain times of the year.

No one is sure how many Ribbon Seals there are, but estimates have ranged from 20,000 to 50,000. It is clear that the species is fairly rare, and has never in historical times been abundant.

Early historical records

The species was first named and described by Zimmerman in 1783. He based his description on a specimen from the Kurile Islands and named it *Phoca fasciata*. The name was subsequently changed to *Histriophoca fasciata* by Pohle in 1932.

Appearance and description

The Ribbon Seal is one of the smaller seals, the males attaining lengths of up to 5 feet 6 inches, and weights of about 210 pounds. The females are a little shorter and weigh up to 180 pounds. Both sexes bear the characteristic 'ribbon' markings, but they are much more conspicuous in the male since their light yellow colour stands out very clearly against the very dark brown fur of the back and flanks (the underparts of the body are yellowish-white in colour). The 'ribbons' form four distinct rings; one around the neck, another around the hind part of the body, and one each side of the body forming large rings around each fore flipper. The ribbons in the female are less distinct because the background coloration is very much lighter than that of the male, being a greyish yellow. The position, size and shape of the ribbons tend to vary more from female to female than they do among the males.

Habitat and general habits

The habits of the species have not been studied. They are known to feed on fish, cephalopods and crustaceans; pollack and squid have been identified in the stomachs of killed animals.

When sighted, the seals are almost invariably solitary or in small groups, and during the parts of the year when the waters are ice-free they are never seen near the shores, and only rarely in the open sea.

Seasonal movements

Scientists believe, without having yet proved it, that the Ribbon Seals make the usual southerly move in the winter, and return north in the following spring and summer.

Reproduction

Adults with pups have only been seen in the Tartar Strait between Sakhalin and the mainland, on floating ice floes. The pupping season appears to occur between March and May and the mating season between the end of July and the beginning of August, after the moult. The gestation period, some authorities suggest, is 280 days.

Birth to maturity

Little information is available about the pups except that before the post-natal moult the fur is long and white in colour. It has been suggested that the pups probably measure 3 feet in length and weigh around 30 pounds. The white coat is shed during April, and the pup is suckled until the time of the adult moult in late June.

The species in relation to man

Alaskan and Russian Eskimos hunt the Ribbon Seal on ice floes and also in the pack ice. The Russian Eskimos or Koryaks hunt specifically for the Ribbon Seal on floes in Penzhina and Gizhiga Bays, while the Alaskan Eskimos catch the species in the course of hunting other species of seal, both on the winter pack ice and also at sea.

The skin of the male seal is greatly prized by the Eskimos who convert it into a 'hold-all' for their waterproof clothing. The skin is removed from the carcass by slitting down the abdomen and removing the pelt as a whole piece. It is then tanned and each side of the slit is provided with holes which are laced together with string, thus making a large and very attractive bag.

THE MONK SEALS

There are, or were, three species of Monk Seal living in widely separated areas of the world — one in the Mediterranean, one in the Hawaiian Islands, and one (which may now be extinct) in the Caribbean. Apart from the Californian Sealion and the Northern Elephant Seal these are the only pinnipeds that live in warm or tropical waters.

The Monk Seals are generally placed by taxonomists in a group of their own. They are, nevertheless, closely allied to the four Antarctic Seals and have similar skeletal characteristics. There are also many superficial similarities between the Bearded Seal of the Arctic and the Monk Seal. Both Bearded and Monk Seals have four mammae and smooth whiskers, unlike other seals; both are fairly sluggish creatures, feeding mainly on molluscs; and both produce pups in alternate years only.

The Monk Seals have an unusual skull. The brain case is approximately equal in length and in breadth, and there is a long parallel-sided inter-orbital region. There are just two incisors and five cheek teeth on each side in the upper and lower jaws.

THE MEDITERRANEAN MONK SEAL   *Monachus monachus*

Distribution and estimated population

The Monk Seal is found throughout most of the Mediterranean Sea, except off some parts of the African coast. Its range extends into the Black Sea, the Adriatic, and out into the Atlantic as far as Maderia and Cap Blanc on the West African coast. But the Mediterranean Monk Seal is by no means a common animal and there are probably less than 5,000 members of the species alive today. It is of sporadic occurrence and seen nowhere regularly. This is hardly surprising, for its haunts are places either totally inaccessible to man or difficult to reach and thus rarely visited. It was recorded in the 1940s on isolated cliffs in Jugoslavia, on the rocky coasts of Sardinia, from the Levant, and on a few sandy islands off the African coasts. It has been spotted in more recent years in the Black Sea, but such sightings are so infrequent that it is not clear how widespread or abundant this species is today.

Early historical records

In historic times the Mediterranean Monk Seal has never been very common, but 2,000 years ago the species was much more abundant than it is now. Aristotle included an accurate account of the Monk Seal in his *Historia Anima-lium*. The seal was given its scientific specific name in 1779 by Hermann, who described a specimen taken on the coast of what is now Jugoslavia as *Phoca monachus*.

Appearance and description

These seals are dark grey with a white or cream coloured belly. Females and immature males are usually lighter in colour than the fully grown male. The hair is short and bristly and in some aged specimens takes on a white appearance. Adults of both sexes measure between 8 and 9 feet in length and may weigh up to 700 pounds. Like the other Monk Seals they have only tiny nails on the hind flippers, but large nails on the fore flippers.

K

Compared to many pinnipeds the Monk Seal has a very short alimentary canal, only some eight times the body length.

Habitat and general habits

Few observations have been made of the habits of wild Mediterranean Monk Seals. But their vocalisations *are* known and are similar to those of a dog. They yelp, bark, and even howl.

They probably feed mainly on flatfish.

Seasonal movements

None, as far as is known.

Reproduction

The pups are born on land in October and November after a gestation period of eleven months. The seals mate shortly after the birth of the pups, but as with the Bearded Seal the recently-pupped cows do not ovulate until after the breeding season is over, and therefore bear pups only in alternate years.

Birth to maturity

At birth the pup is about 3 feet long and weighs around 45 pounds. The coat is woolly and dark brown in colour; sometimes it shades to yellow on the underside of the body. The pup is believed to stay with the cow for up to three years. By the time it is four years old it is sexually mature and will mate at that age.

The species in relation to man

Not for many years have Monk Seals been plentiful enough to be hunted but in former times they were of considerable use to the inhabitants of coasts and islands in at least some parts of their range. Monk Seal bones have been found among paleolithic remains in Italy — an indication, probably, that early man ate seals.

Even before the Classical epoch the ancient Greeks hunted seals. In her account of the Monk Seals, Judith E. King gives many examples of the effect that the seals of the Mediterranean have had on the lives and superstitions of the inhabitants. Towns have been named after them — there is a Foca in Turkey, and a Foca in Jugoslavia, called after the Greek *Phoca,* the 'Plump Animal'. Part of ancient Greece, north of Corinth, was named Phocis and it was within this district that Mount Parnassus stood.

Superstitions about the seals were legion. Fishermen wore sealskin boots and clothing to protect themselves against lightning. A seal skin carried round a field and hung on the farmer's door would protect the crops in that field from hailstones. Insomnia could be cured by putting the flipper from a seal's right side under the pillow. Seals were specially protected both by Poseidon, the God of the Sea, and by the Sun God, Apollo.

Among classical writers who mention seals (and it must be the Mediterranean Monk Seal to which they refer) are Pliny, Plutarch and Homer. In the *Odyssey* Homer relates how a dead woman's body was thrown overboard from a ship 'for the Seals'. In ancient times at any rate the seal was a sufficiently familiar and favoured beast for its portrait to appear on coins.

Mediæval sailors knew the seals and killed them for their skins. We know that in 1341 seal skins were being used in the Canary Islands. In the fifteenth century there was a regular industry based on the taking of seals' skins off the Barbary Coast.

The species in captivity

The first Monk Seal recorded in captivity was shown in France and Germany in 1760. Seventeen years later there were at least two in captivity. One was a female and was exhibited at Nimes, and the other, a male, was captured in the Adriatic and shown in France. It lived for two years, quite an achievement for a marine creature in those days, and was shown during that time to King Louis XVI.

In this country single specimens arrived at the London Zoo in 1884 and in 1910. Both were caught in Madeira.

THE HAWAIIAN MONK SEAL (Plate 16)   *Monachus schauinslandi*

Distribution and estimated population

The Hawaiian Monk Seal inhabits isolated atolls in the western Hawaiian islands. The present population is believed to be between 1,000 and 1,500. In 1958 it was estimated to be 1,350.

Appearance and description

These seals are between 7 and 8 feet in length. The females are on average some 8 inches longer than the males and may weigh up to 5 hundredweights. Both sexes are dark grey-brown above, shading to a lighter tone or white underneath. The head is broad and the eyes are large and protruding, very watery when on land, and with a rather vacant bovine stare. All the flippers (including the hind flippers) are small and useless for locomotion on land, and the seal has to progress as best it can by wriggling and shuffling along on its belly.

Habitat and general habits

The seals bask on beaches during the day and move off to the water at night to swim and fish lazily in the shallow waters around the atolls where they live. Not the speediest of swimmers, Hawaiian Monk Seals capture mostly slow moving octopuses and reef fish living on the sea bed.

Seasonal movements

As might be expected in an animal living in such tropical latitudes there are no seasonal movements.

Reproduction

The pupping season is not clearly defined and pups are born from December to March, the greatest number in the last month.

Birth to maturity

The pup is 3 feet long at birth and covered with a black woolly coat. During the last weeks of the five-week lactation period this coat moults and is replaced by dark brown fur with silver-tipped hairs and dirty white underparts.

The species in relation to man

In the nineteenth century the Hawaiian Monk Seal suffered the same mass slaughter as many of the other fur seals in the world. The first recorded sealing expedition to Hawaii was in 1824 by the brig *Ainoa*, which took the seals for their oil and pelts. The seals were easy to kill as they lay quietly basking on the beaches and it was not long before other sealers came to the islands to get rich on this new source of quick profits. During the next few years thousands of these inoffensive and trusting seals were slaughtered. In a few years the population had dwindled so drastically that it was no longer worth hunting the seal commercially, and the sealing grounds were deserted. The species was then thought to be practically extinct, but in 1859 the vessel *Gambia* sailed into Honolulu harbour after a sealing expedition with 1,500 seal skins and 240 barrels of oil in her holds. This was a great surprise to everybody, but no one believed the species could have survived such an immense haul. Fortunately, they were wrong.

A small remnant of the original seal population of the Hawaiian islands remained undetected and unmolested by the predatory sealers. In 1909, fifty years after the species was thought to have become extinct, the United States Government declared the islands a protected area — the Hawaiian Bird Reservation — and since then the seals have been safe. From the small surviving remnant the seal population has slowly grown over the years; in 1924 there were 400 of them; today there are probably three times as many.

THE CARIBBEAN MONK SEAL   *Monachus tropicalis*

Distribution and estimated population

The Caribbean Monk Seal inhabited the shores of small islands in the

Bahamas, the Gulf of Mexico, the Caribbean Sea and off the coast of Florida. It is not certain whether or not any of these seals have survived to the present day. There can only be a very few of them if they exist at all.

Early historical records

The Caribbean Monk Seal was one of the first mammals of the New World ever to be described by early navigators. There is some doubt whether the distinction of being the very first belongs to the seal or to a rat that was seen on Haiti. In August 1494 Columbus anchored off the island of Alta Vela to the south of Haiti; when his men went ashore they found 'sea-wolves' sleeping on the sand, and they killed eight of them for food. Later explorers also saw seals on the islands and in 1675 Dampier wrote in his *Voyage to the Bay of Campeachy* (off the Alacrane Reef) — 'Here are many Seals: they come up to sun themselves on only two or three of the Islands, I don't know exactly [if they are] of the same kind with those in colder Climates, but . . . . they always live where there is Plenty of Fish.' In those days there were thousands of seals to be seen in the Caribbean.

Appearance and description

Specimens of the Caribbean Monk Seal are 7 to 8 feet long, and the female is slightly smaller than the male. They are brown in colour, but sometimes the fur is grizzled. The underparts are cream. It is recorded that the whiskers are yellowish, and the iris of the eye reddish-brown.

Habitat and habits

The Caribbean Monk Seal was a lethargic beast, especially on land, and its inactivity made its capture very easy. It fed, in all probability, on slow-moving reef fish; and it normally led such a still and torpid life that algae grew over its fur — greenish-coloured specimens were quite a common sight. (Observers have also seen algae growing over the Hawaiian Monk Seal.)

The Caribbean species was said to be very difficult to arouse, and the attitude of the animals when attacked was either one of unconcern or indecision. Because of their unsuspicious nature and the lack of lustre in their eyes they had the reputation of being very stupid.

In spite of their lethargy the seals were vociferous. Their voices had the same attributes as those of dogs, and they were capable of barking, snarling, growling and grunting in a variety of ways.

Seasonal movements

This seal did not (or does not) migrate.

Reproduction

Pups have been seen in early December. Otherwise next to nothing is known about the reproductive biology of this species.

Birth to maturity

All that is known is that the few pups that have ever been seen and written about were around 3 feet in length and covered with a coat of black woolly fur.

The species in relation to man

Once their presence was known the West Indian Seals were subjected to constant depredation. Dampier in 1675 remarked '. . . . there being here such Plenty of Fowls and Seals (especially of the latter) that the Spaniards do often come hither to make Oyl of their Fat' and that 'it has been visited by Englishmen from Jamaica, particularly by Captain Long: who having the Command of a small Bark, came hither purposely to make Seal-Oyl.'

Forty years later sealing was already a major occupation in the Caribbean. Sir Hans Sloane in his *History of Jamaica* said that 'the Bahama Islands are filled with Seals, sometimes Fishers will catch one hundred in a night. They fry or melt them, and bring off their oil for Lamps to the Islands.'

In the nineteenth century the seals were hunted even more intensively and by 1885 there was scarcely a seal to be seen in the Caribbean. By then thousands of them had been slaughtered for their oil, meat and hides.

Over the last eighty years fewer and fewer Caribbean Monk Seals have been seen. Some were spotted on the coast of Texas and near isolated bays during the present century; but since 1949, when two of them were seen off Jamaica, the Caribbean Monk Seal has not been definitely recorded. Lighthousekeepers have sometimes heard sounds like the barking of seals but scientists have found no trace of the creatures. They may well be extinct.

The species in captivity

Several specimens of *Monachus tropicalis* have been kept in captivity in the New York Aquarium. In 1897 the Aquarium received two Monk Seals and, in spite of their reputation for lack of intelligence, one of these animals rapidly learned to fill its cheeks with water and squirt it at the visitors. This specimen was caught at the Red Snapper Banks off Yucatan and lived in captivity for $5\frac{1}{2}$ years. At the end of this time it was 7 feet long, and weighed 25 stone.

In 1909 New York received some more Caribbean Monk Seals — an adult male and three yearlings. These, too, were playful creatures and one of them used its fore flippers to spray water over onlookers.

Appendix I
Checklist of the Pinnipedia

IN COMPILING this list several authorities have been consulted, principally *Seals of the World* by Judith E. King, published by the Trustees of the British Museum (Natural History) in 1964; and *The Mammals* by Desmond Morris, published by Hodder and Stoughton in 1965. The scientific and English names are followed by a summary of the present distribution of each species and the latest estimate of its world numbers.

Family: OTARIIDAE

Callorhinus ursinus (Linnaeus 1758).
Northern, Pribilof or Alaskan Fur Seal. N. Pacific, breeding Pribilofs (main colony), Commander and Robben Is., Kuriles. c. 2,000,000.

Arctocephalus australis (Zimmerman 1783).
South American or Southern Fur Seal. Three races round S. American coasts, one breeding S. Brazil to Peru, one Falkland Is., one Galapagos. c. 100,000.

Arctocephalus philippii (Peters 1866).
Philippi or Guadalupe Fur Seal. One race extinct Juan Fernandez, Chile; one on Guadalupe off S. California. c. 500.

Arctocephalus pusillus (Schreber 1776).
South African or Cape Fur Seal. Coasts of southern Africa, breeding islands off Cape Province and S.W. Africa. c. 500,000.

Arctocephalus doriferus (Wood Jones 1925).
Australian Fur Seal. Coasts of Great Australian Bight. Numbers unknown but believed to be increasing.

Arctocephalus tasmanicus (Scott and Lord 1926). Tasmanian Fur Seal. Coasts of Tasmania, N.S. Wales and Victoria, breeding on four island groups. At least 12,000.

Arctocephalus forsteri (Lesson 1828).
New Zealand Fur Seal. Coasts and Islands of New Zealand south to Macquarie. c. 50,000, increasing.

Arctocephalus tropicalis (Gray 1872).
Kerguelen Fur Seal. Two races in Indian and S. Atlantic Oceans; one breeding Gough I. (Tristan da Cunha group) and elsewhere; one breeding Bird I. off S. Georgia and neighbouring islands. At least 40,000.

Eumetopias jubatus (Schreber 1776).
Northern or Steller's Sealion. N. Pacific
and Bering Sea; breeding Aleutians and
coasts on both sides Pacific. c. 300,000.

Zalophus californianus (Lesson 1828).
Californian Sealion. Three races; one
Californian coast (c. 50,000); one Galapagos (c. 20,000); one Honshu, Japan
(c. 300).

Otaria byronia (Blainville 1820).
Southern Sealion. Pacific and Atlantic
coasts of S. America and large colony
Falkland Is. c. 800,000.

Neophoca cinerea (Péron 1816).
Australian Sealion. Coasts and Islands
of Great Australian Bight. 2,000 to
10,000.

Phocarctos hookeri (Gray 1844).
Hooker's Sealion. Mainly on Auckland
and Campbell Is. south of New Zealand.
10,000 to 50,000.

Family: ODOBENIDAE

Odobenus rosmarus (Linnaeus 1758).
Walrus. Two races in Pacific and
Atlantic within Arctic circle; one on
coasts of N.E. Siberia and N.W. Alaska;
one from Greenland to Nova Zemlya.
45,000 to 90,000.

Family: PHOCIDAE

Sub-family: CYSTOPHORINAE

Mirounga leonina (Linnaeus 1758).
Southern Elephant Seal. Sub-Antarctic
islands and mainland, large colonies S.

Georgia, Kerguelen and Macquarie.
600,000 to 700,000.

Mirounga angustirotris (Gill 1866).
Northern Elephant Seal. Islands off
coasts of California and Mexico, wandering north and south. 10,000 to 15,000.

Cystophora cristata (Erxleben 1777).
Bladdernose or Hooded Seal. Arctic and
N. Atlantic Oceans from Bear I. to
Labrador and Newfoundland. 300,000
to 500,000.

Sub-family: LOBODONTINAE

Hydrurga leptonyx (Blainville 1820).
Leopard Seal. Antarctic ice and sub-
Antarctic islands northwards to Australia,
New Zealand and S. America. At least
200,000.

Leptonychotes weddelli (Lesson 1826).
Weddell Seal. Most southerly species,
breeding Antarctic ice; wanders north
and a few breed S. Orkneys. 200,000
to 500,000.

Ommatophoca rossi (Gray 1844).
Ross Seal. Antarctica south of 60 degrees.
c. 20,000.

Lobodon carcinophagus (Hombron and Jacquinot 1842).
Crabeater Seal. Antarctica, wandering
northwards. 2,000,000 to 5,000,000.

Sub-family: PHOCINAE

Phoca vitulina (Linnaeus 1758).
Common or Harbour Seal. N. Atlantic
and N. Pacific: from Portugal to New

York; from California to Japan; isolated colony in freshwater lakes in Canada. No figure available.

Halichoerus grypus (Fabricius 1791). Grey Seal. Breeds Baltic; Norway, N.E. Europe; British Isles (34,200) to Iceland; N.W. Atlantic. 52,500.

Erignathus barbatus (Erxleben 1777). Bearded Seal. Arctic ice, coming south in Pacific to Hokkaido, Japan; in Atlantic to Nova Scotia; vagrant Britain and France. c. 100,000.

Pusa hispida (Schreber 1775). Ringed Seal. Ten races named in Arctic seas and ice; Sea of Okhotsk; Baltic; freshwater lakes in Finland and Russia. 2,500,000 to 6,000,000.

Pusa caspica (Gmelin 1788). Caspian Sea, breeding in north. Over 1,000,000.

Pusa sibirica (Gmelin 1788). Baikal Seal. Lake Baikal, Siberia, mainly in northern waters. 40,000 to 100,000.

Pagophilus groenlandicus (Erxleben 1777). Harp Seal. N. Atlantic and Arctic Oceans from N. Russia to Greenland, Newfoundland and Hudson Bay; breeding mainly White Sea, Greenland Sea and Gulf of St Lawrence; vagrant to Britain. Over 5,000,000.

Histriophoca fasciata (Zimmerman 1783). Banded or Ribbon Seal. N. Pacific: west Bering Sea to Arctic and south to Sakhalin. 20,000 to 50,000.

Sub-family: MONACHINAE

Monachus monachus (Hermann 1779). Mediterranean Monk Seal. Mediterranean and Black Seas; Atlantic to Madeira. Less than 5,000.

Monachus schauinslandi (Matschie 1905). Hawaiian Monk Seal. West Hawaiian islands. 1,000 to 1,500.

Monachus tropicalis (Gray 1850). Caribbean or West Indian Monk Seal. Formerly on islands in Caribbean Sea; may be extinct.

Appendix II   Books About Seals

My collaborators and I consulted a great many books and scientific papers during research for this book. But for the general reader the following short list of modern, easily accessible books will be more helpful as a guide to further study of seals, especially of the two British species. Those by Nina Warner Hooke, H. G. Hurrell and R. H. Pearson deal with remarkable relationships established between seals and humans.

H. R. Hewer
    Grey Seals. London: Sunday Times Book Publications, 1962

Grace Hickling
    Grey Seals and the Farne Islands. London: Routledge & Kegan Paul, 1962

Nina Warner Hooke
    The Seal Summer. London: Arthur Barker, 1964

H. G. Hurrell
    Atlanta My Seal. London: William Kimber, 1963

Judith E. King
    Seals of the World. London: British Museum (Natural History), 1964

R. M. Lockley
    The Seals and the Curragh. Dent, 1954
    Grey Seal, Common Seal. London: Andre Deutsch, 1966

L. Harrison Matthews
    Sea Elephant. London: Macgibbon & Kee, 1952

R. H. Pearson
    A Seal Flies By. Hart-Davis, 1959

Victor B. Scheffer
    Seals, Sea lions and Walruses. Stanford, Calif.: Stanford University Press, 1958

David Thomson
    The People of the Sea. Revised Edition. London: Barrie & Rockcliffe, 1965

Appendix II   Books About Seals